Stories from the Age of Covid

Edited By

Glenn Steckler & Larry Steckler

E-Mail: lartronics@aol.com

HOW THIS BOOK CAME TO BE

Virginia Beach, Virginia & ***Telluride, Colorado*** — Watching the news throughout the pandemic, 87 year-old Larry Steckler and his son, Glenn Steckler were struck by the growing number of people in need: long lines at food banks, people getting evicted, hospitals overflowing with patients. Their goal is to raise money through the sale of this book to help fund food bank efforts and address the increased demands put on them by the Covid-19 pandemic.

Submissions to this book are as small as a paragraph or two, or as large as many pages. Some contributions are funny, some are sad, but all are real and come from personal experiences and observations.

Types of submissions we have included are:

- Short anecdotes
- Stories about particular incidents
- Feelings, worries, musings
- Hopes for once this is over, a view of the future
- How the pandemic has changed lives and affected goals
- How relationships have been affected for better and for worse
- What things have been done to cope
- Subjects related to health, athletics, hobbies, cooking, travel, loss . . . .

We have read, edited and included many different kinds of contributions and we send our sincere thanks to all who have taken the time and made the effort to submit their thoughts and experiences.

Foreword

We would like to thank all of the people who contributed to this collection. Obviously, we could not have done this without you. Thank you for generously donating your time, energy, effort and creativity to join together in the success of this book. To share your personal thoughts and stories is our honor and we appreciate you entrusting them to us.

There were three main impetuses to launching this project. First of all, out of selfishness. Putting this book together was a way for father and son to bridge the distance between where Glenn lives near Telluride, Colorado and where Larry resides in Virginia Beach, Virginia. Watching how Eugene and Daniel Levy worked together to launch and produce Shitt$ Creek may have planted a seed in our brains that grew into this book idea. This book is a way to fill some of the void that the Covid-19 pandemic has created in our lives, to fight that feeling of helplessness and uncertainty that many of us have experienced, and create a sense of control over at least one small part of our lives.

Secondly, we thought that giving people an outlet to express their stories and feelings would be therapeutic for many. Writing down one's story, expressing one's emotions through this book, we felt would be an effective addition to the things we have all been doing to get through this time.

For some the coping mechanism is exercise. For others it is having someone to talk with. Maybe your distraction is learning a new recipe, taking up a new hobby, spending more time with family, catching up on all the novels and movies you never had time for, or dipping into the liquor cabinet more often than normal times call for... Our hope is that this project would give each of the authors yet another outlet in the mosaic of coping strategies.

Finally, we wanted to see if the work we put into publishing this collection could do some good. Food is a basic need and in the richest country on the planet it is difficult to accept that there are families, children, and seniors that do not have enough to eat.

According to www.feedingamerica.org and the USDA's Household Food Insecurity in the United States report, "...more than 35 million people in the United States struggled with hunger in 2019." And feedingamerica.org goes on to state, "Due to the effects of the coronavirus pandemic, more than 50 million people may experience food insecurity, including a potential 17 million children." The HuffPost adds, "In late April [2020], slightly more than 20% — or 1 in 5 — U.S. households reported food insecurity, according to an analysis by The Brookings Institution. By comparison, 11% of U.S. households were considered food insecure in 2018, according to the latest data from the U.S. Department of Agriculture. 'Overall rates of household food insecurity have effectively doubled,' Brookings wrote in its report."

As a result, since the coronavirus hit the U.S. in earnest in March 2020, there has been a sharp increase in demand at food banks nationwide. Our aim is to have this collection of creative works, that you are about to delve into, provide a new and additional funding source for food banks to meet the current increase in demand that they are experiencing.

We are very proud of the collection we have put together. In the following pages you will find stories, poetry, memories and remembrances that will paint a picture of our combined experiences during the Age of Covid. You will read a rich variety of perspectives that only scratch the surface of what we have all endured. We hope that the collaboration presented between these two covers will inspire you to live your own best story.

Glenn Steckler and Larry Steckler

Yes, things sure are different now. Covid mornings begin, like every other morning, yet there are differences.

"Family" tells us just how different life has become because of the effects of this deadly virus that is just starting to be controlled. It has infected millions of people around the world, but while vaccines are becoming available, the dire, sometimes killing, effects still linger on.

Sharing personal experiences,
our authors found peacefulness, creativity,
balance and learning.

Family

Tucking In My Daughter in a Time of Corona Virus

by Rosemerry Wahtola Trommer

And because she is wise
in the ways the young are,
my daughter, frightened and weeping,
asked between sobs
for a happy story.

There are times when a story
is the best remedy —
not because it takes us away
from the truth but because
it leads us closer in.

I told her the story of her birth,
and we laughed until
it was my turn to cry as I realized
no matter how scary the world,
what a miracle, the birth of a child.

Then, as fear made a sneaky return,
we whispered a list of things we
were grateful for, falling asleep with these
words on our breaths: cats, books, rivers,
home, family, soft blankets, music.

Things Are A Lot Different

by Bryson Livesay

Things are a lot different since we got out of school in March, 2020. School shut down all of a sudden. I thought we were going to be out for a few days. We haven't been back since then. We cannot go out to do the things we used to do. If we do go out, anywhere, we have to wear a mask. Everybody is supposed to stay six feet apart. A lot of places closed down – businesses of all kinds -- recreation centers, movie theatres, and even many stores.

A lot of people have lost their jobs. Some of the restaurants that are open only have their drive-through open. Movie theaters are closed down too. We have to wash our hands and use hand sanitizer every time we do anything. It makes me nervous when I go into a store and wear my mask, just because I know someone else in there might be carrying the Coronavirus. Instead, I stay home most of the time.

At first, it was scary to watch the things about the pandemic on TV. There are a lot of people with Covid-19. It is still scary because it is still out there and anyone can catch it. We have had to be careful about who we go around with and who we visit. I haven't seen my friends or my older cousins very much since it started.

The only thing I like about this is that we can stay at home. I have more time to play with my toys and play outside. I don't have to get up as early to set off for school and to get on the bus. I get to see my baby cousins every day when my mom babysits them. My mom is home with us during the week and works on some weekends. She is a nurse. My dad still has to work a lot.

We were supposed to go on a big trip in April, but it got canceled too. I played outside a lot this summer. My Grandma has a pool so we got to splash around in it a lot. I did get to go on a vacation this summer. We went to White Lake, NC for a week. It was not as fun as it usually is because the arcade and carnival were closed. We could go there because we weren't around a lot of people.

I don't really like school online because they give us a lot of work. It is kind of hard to find the assignments. Sometimes the internet connection is not good. I do like that we get out of school earlier than real school. I do miss seeing my friends and teachers in person. I like that I can see my friends and teachers on Zoom.

I am excited for Christmas. We are still going to spend that day together with my family. I want to go to Surge when the pandemic is over. It is a trampoline park. I hope we will still be able to go on our trip in 2021.

My Father

by Suzanne Cheavens

My father
Were he alive today
Would have no patience
For the altered state of myth-swilling
and shuttered minds,
For the feces-flinging mobs
armed with Old Glory
that proud symbol,
now flecked with spittle,
used as a cudgel.
The fetid air
reeks of hatred for
any face that deviates
from their own
pale, fat moons.
Horned fanaticism
Ignored factualism
Fall
Into the chasm
Never to be heard from again.

My father
Speaks through me now
He dove into science

As if it would save his life
-- and it did –
Now I say for him,
Your ignorance on matters of our struggling planet
and unchecked virulence
Will be the death of us all.
Your puny pistol cannot stand down
voracious fires
flooded lungs
You will drown in your own refusal
of the hot, hard truth.

My father
Would have given up on our species by now.
Perhaps he'd deign to lift his voice
To make another appeal for reason,
but lack of reason is madness
and it is madness
that drives the gabbling rabble.
You've lost the script, my father might say.
You think it's about rights
but you're wrong.
Watch the bellwether species
Not your false idols
For what comes next.
I hope the hour of our demise is not upon us.
Perhaps it's already arrived.

My father
Can be spared of our ugly, unholy deeds.
He dances
Among the stars.
The only true freedom.

Covid Kids

by Kerri P.

There is one vivid memory from this time that always makes me smile and I pull up this image in my mind on those particularly challenging days. It reminds me that while some aspects of life are more difficult, there are benefits to staying home and being with family.

It was some weeks into the first semester of virtual learning at our house. It was mid-morning and I turned to see my youngest child walk into the kitchen to get a snack. She had her earphones in, holding her laptop like a serving tray, but she was only wearing a t-shirt and underwear.

When I went to check on the other kids, I noticed my next oldest child was at the dining room table, in class, wearing her pajamas.

I returned to the kitchen just in time to witness my son take a seat at the table in front of his laptop, where he promptly pulled up the hood on his sweatshirt to cover the fact that he had not yet brushed his hair that day or changed out of his pajamas.

Personal Experiences

by Peggy Cross

Overall I have found this time of Covid-19 to be one of peacefulness for me, and creativity and balance. And learning. I know being an introvert makes this easier, from a physical perspective.

Within my family of origin and marriage, I have wonderful relationships with my children, with whom I talk weekly, and a sister.....our conversations are close to daily. My brother was just buried last week which brought some grief, but mostly relief, due to his mental condition. We had talked about dying, and how neither of us was attached to whether we left or stayed. I have found new connections of which I was unaware, between people I have known for ages. Keeping and renewing decades old friendly contacts has been awesome, leading to newfound friends with marvelous gifts to share on Zoom.

During this Age of Covid, I have seen my friends enhance their various creative skills and overcome reluctance, on the part of many, to share them with the world. These include architects, jewelry designers and crafters, writers, musicians and developing leaders. These are blessings of what I am finding to be of great interest and quality that are now shared and that, two or three months ago, were not.

Another benefit of Covid is seeing my life patterns......costs and benefits if you will......to the experiences of this lifetime. Oh, I also decided this past summer to live to be 100 years-of-age, rather than 90, which was what I had decided when I was just 45. Yes, it has been a very good year.

Family Togetherness

by Larry Steckler

Family visits changed as Covid-19 came home to roost. It sure changed how families gathered. For us there was what has become a new way to catch up. Yes, we did still talk regularly using our phones, but we wanted more and we found it.

Every second Sunday we log in to Zoom and get to see and hear each other. On the next page is a photo of what one of our morning gatherings look like. All of my children, and sometimes some of my grandchildren, log in and join has become a regularly scheduled family video visit.

We start at 11:00-am east-coast time. Seated in front of our computers we get to spend an hour or so just catching up. In the photo on the next page you can see what my screen reveals once we have all logged in. (Kerri in Houston, with her youngest peeking over her shoulder; myself here in Virginia Beach, my youngest daughter Adria from Hicksville, New York, my son Glenn from Telluride, Colorado, and my eldest daughter Gail, also in Virginia Beach.)

We update each other on all the latest family news, both home and work, and I get the latest info on events and activities.

Zoom Time!
Staying in touch – via electronics

Zoom also makes it possible for me to join in morning prayers virtually from the synagogue at 8:00-am. Currently Covid keeps us from meeting in person. Yes, it is not the same as being out and around, but it sure does break up the monotony of being indoors – day after day after day.

We are all very familiar with the term social distancing and being "Socially Distant" has become a common experience during the pandemic.

One special experience faced during the Covid pandemic is quarantine! You will read one person's experience with what that is like.

Other works speak about walking in someone else's shoes, how unchanging days seem to blend into one long never-ending time and how confinement changes people. We develop new personalities, new feelings. And we may or may not like the changes.

Covid takes its toll. The walls of our world are closing in. Yet the end is in sight and a return to normal, or a new normal, is on the way. Perhaps this is the mood we sit in as we wait for the vaccine to release us from our confinement.

Finally, does being cooped up affect the human mind? This section may help you reach a conclusion to respond to that question.

Socially Distanced

Fathom
by Daiva Chesonis

(San Miguel County, CO. Poet Laureate 2019-2022)

Safe distance they say
The length of a ski
The depth of a coffin

Fear lives within that fathom
While aloofness is all the rage
Displayed like seashells on a beach

Six feet apart they say
Twelve inches for each of our senses
Each clicking into focus
Into chaos and quiet and the homecooked
Our sense of touch washed away
    with soap for 20 seconds
I just
    wanna kiss
        my fiancé
Not back long enough to risk it

May there be spaces in your togetherness
    Gibran said

May there be wellness in our isolation
he might add

The length of a ski
The depth of a coffin
Safe distance they say

March 23, 2020

Dated because it's important to know where we were when.

Quarantined!

by Justin Criado

I haven't left my place for 10 days. My hair is growing wildly over my ears and curling at the nape of my neck. My beard is even more unruly, as I'm reverting back to the ugly Homo sapiens. I am — more of a caveman-like creature with terrible posture and a unibrow. But instead of plucking edible plants from the ground or clubbing my next meal to death, I have a freezer full of Lean Cuisines and pizzas.

Walking my trash to the garage has become an exciting adventure of sorts that I consider "travel" at the moment. But this is what we must do. The government doesn't ask us to stay home and essentially do nothing for the greater good of humanity often, so don't mess it up.

It's also nice to finally know the term for what I've been practicing for most of my adult life. Social distancing isn't only an effective way to combat the virus, but also my new excuse for not hanging out with anyone after all of this passes. At least I won't have to make up bold-faced lies, like I twisted my ankle getting off the pot or I'm hanging out with a lady friend, anymore.

Essentially every aspect of our everyday lives has been affected. It's weird to see a Burger King commercial about best "minimum contact" practices. "Let us take care of you as you take care of yourself," is the fast-food chain's new motto. Never mind a Whopper is 677 calories, including 37 grams of saturated fat (56 percent of the recommended daily intake of such poison) and 87 mg of cholesterol (29 percent). "Let us kill you slowly as you wither away on your couch crippled with anxiety and fear for the foreseeable future" sounds more like it. The King's other new ad partially speaks to that in saluting all the "couch potatriots" out there.

Thankfully, the closest Burger King, or any fast food, is 66 miles away in Montrose, (This author resided in Telluride, Colorado) which might as well be Mars.

Speaking of intergalactic travel, my parents, who are both in their late 50s, are back in Pittsburgh. Dad's still working; Mum isn't. I love them, but they're stubborn. My sister and I have been hounding them about not going out in public for anything other than essentials. They informed us Easter ham and spark plugs for the motorcycle are essential. They're getting better. If anything happens to them, devil be damned, I imagine a chaotic scenario where I drop everything and hop into my car and drive across the country like Mad Max, fending off all the derelicts and degenerates who look like Joe Exotic along the way. I'd arrive back home a road hardened, post-apocalyptic warrior with skulls dangling from my belt and dried blood smeared under my eyes; a primal byproduct of these strange and terrible times.

In reality, however, I'm taking this time to catch up on reading, with a goal to finish at least one book a week. I also started an "extinction journal" to document all of this. Maybe the future aliens will find it useful. I stopped watching the White House virus debriefings and reading the headlines of the national papers. I started listening to black metal before noon, and enjoying a cup of black coffee and a bowl of bud before bed. My place, which is less than 1,000 square feet, has never been cleaner. I've even wiped down the baseboards. I'm also a pro at washing dishes, like, every day. The hum of the machine is almost like the white noise of public side conversations. Also learned that eating more than one Lean Cuisine per sitting defeats the purpose of ingesting them in the first place.

Fortunately, I am still working, which is probably saving me from pure, eye-gouging insanity. Covering the pandemic can be a lot, but it's necessary and crucial.

Back to the present, it's noon the day of deadline. Let's wrap this up and get on with it. I scroll Instagram briefly. A post from the British daily the Guardian pops up.

"The horror films got it wrong. This virus has turned us into caring neighbours," wrote journalist George Monbiot.

The whole ordeal is oddly inspiring. Seemingly everyone is lending a helping hand, yes, even Burger King. John Krasinski's new weekly web show "Some Good News" has become a highlight of my week, if not a reason to openly weep. Check it out if you need a pick-me-up.

But my bloodshot eyes remind me that there is still work to be done. Someone has to cover the end of the world.

Other Shoes
by Rosemerry Wahtola Trommer

We all belong to the same galactic oneness.
—Carlos Santana, Master Class

I could be the doctor who, overwhelmed
in the ER, went home and killed herself.
I could be the sixteen-year-old boy
who had to cover his father with a white sheet
before the coroner arrived.
I could be the white sheet.
I could be the lawmaker unable to sleep,
or her pillow that hears her cry out in fear
when at last the sleep arrives.
I could be the rhythmic hissing of the ventilator
or the wail of the wife, or the weary hum
of the custodian beneath her mask
as she wipes the surfaces clean.
It could be me, the eleventh death
in the town next door to mine.
It could be me, the one who
unknowingly makes you sick
because I don't know I carry
something deadly inside my breath.
And so I don't hug you when I see you

across the post office lobby,
though my heart leaps up to hold you.
Because you could be the flat line
on the EKG.
Because you could be number twelve.

Website: wordwoman.com
Daily poetry blog: A Hundred Falling Veils
Podcast on creative process: Emerging Form

Hunker down
by Suzanne Cheavens

(Previously published in the Telluride Daily Planet, October 21, 2020)

In a turn of events beyond anything I could have possibly imagined, I am writing my umpteenth newspaper column on my birthday during a pandemic. Given that it's a proletarian Tuesday makes it no less remarkable. Despite the chaotic state of the planet and of this nation in particular, I find myself oddly calm. Relax, reads a poster in the Dearly Beloved's office, nothing is in control. It took a pandemic to achieve this state.

I consider myself exceedingly fortunate to not only be working, but to be working from home. In being in the same place literally every waking and sleeping hour of my life, my home has taken on an even greater significance. BP (Before Pandemic), it was a weekend dalliance, a place where a week's worth of choring would be crammed into two days (I mean, who feels like getting after domestic duties during the work week when a commute is factored in? Pas moi.), the more elaborate meals would be crafted, and when the broken got repaired. DP (During Pandemic) the humble abode is shipshape, my unbroken presence ensuring the washing machine hums, the dishwasher is loaded, the meals prepped, the floor Hoovered. My home has always been my sanctum sanctorum. Now it is a wellspring of contentment, a buffer of happiness and love against the barbed edges of the world out there. I am no domestic goddess — I have always said when I'm lying on my deathbed, I will not be fretting about cobwebs — but I have used the spare time in between the hours of sitting that is a writer's life to push a vacuum, start a stock, cuddle a feline, hit the trail. When the Dearly Beloved returns at the end of his day, he enters a veritable nest.

The home that has evolved in this historic era of our lives has become the replacement for everything I miss — theater work, concerts, the easy camaraderie of a drink at "The Buck" with friends. As flagrantly social as I am, I have become a devoted isolationist. I've hosted a few folks on the patio and visited some chums on sunny decks, but relative to the BP level of my social life, I am downright monkish, and perfectly fine with that, it must be said.

With worrisome winter a hellhound on my tail, I anticipate seeing far less of the few I've seen. The virus that has brought us to our knees feasts on an indoor environment, and so we devise ways to extend the season outdoors. The need for some human interaction is both desired and necessary. We've invested in woolen blankets and are shopping heaters. I'd prefer the coziness of a chiminea, but our HOA frowns on flaming anything. Still, the patio will only reasonably take us through Thanksgiving, if we're lucky. I envision a long, hunkered-down winter.

Human connectivity has taken on a different hue. The ubiquitous Zoom meetings are where I join with the government officials who are guiding our communities through the pandemic. I'm involved with "The Listening Club," also on Zoom, a book club for album lovers, and a gathering that I can tell just after a single session will help my groove abide. We all need to unmute ourselves from time to time and share our passions.

Social media is a lifeline I crave and abhor, almost in equal measure. I post poetry, music and photos to rise above the squalor of unkindness that threatens to undermine my sometimes-unsure grasp on sanity. But through social media, I stay current with far-flung friends, be it Spain, Brooklyn, Maryland, Texas or Norwood. I am reminded that, wherever we are, we are all at home and missing life BP.

Social media shines on birthdays. It serves as a digital reminder so that we can send our good wishes to the birthday boy or girl on a day that, in my estimation, should be each of our own, national holidays. Today, as I write, my devices are a Vesuvius of good tidings from yes, Spain, Brooklyn, Maryland, Texas and Norwood. Ensconced in my abode, I am by turns laughing and crying, and to paraphrase The Stone Roses, feeling adored.

The happy revisitation of one's natal day is a time for reflection. The year 2020 will reverberate for eons. Some people are giving the year a vigorous upthrust of the middle finger, and while there are days when I would join that salute, there are far more days I offer up my gratitude. I'm healthy, I'm working and have, in my union with the Dearly Beloved, found a richness and closeness I'm not sure would have been possible without the pandemic playing its troubling hand. These are times that call on my natural optimism and resiliency. It's true that I have wallowed in some bleak places, but more often a good meal, baseball on the TV, an elongated hour on the guitar or a sticky wicket of a crossword puzzle will keep the train on the tracks. And, of course, look where I live! A well-timed forest bath is my drug of choice.

It is said that in a time of crisis we see the best of what humans can be. And while not all humans rise to the top, I think many do. As we retreat to our dens for the winter, we will face the challenge of how to stay connected and healthy. In our community, a tribe of creative, compassionate people, I am confident we will emerge closer than ever. Here's to better days.

One-sided Conversation with the COVID-19 Coronavirus (with apologies to Dr. Seuss)

by Lynda La Rocca

(This poem originally appeared in *The Colorado Sun*)

I do not like you, so you see
I wish that you would go away —
don't come again another day.
I do not like you, COVID v.

I do not like you, this is true
because the only thing you do
is make us sick and disrupt lives
of friends and families, husbands, wives.

You make us stay inside when we
have lots of things to do and see.
You make us hoard hand sanitizers,
and turn us into greedy misers
piling toilet-paper rolls
into closets, hidey-holes.
We're doing social distancing,
have turned to online conferencing,
but I do not like this way of being
or all the tragedy I'm seeing.
So I'll repeat myself to say:
Covid-19; go away!

The Same Day – Again, and again, and. . . . .
by Chester H. Lawrence

My alarm announced the break of my new day, but I am not sure what day today is. My calendar tells me it is Sunday, day 124 since the fear of Covid has forced me to remain in-doors. And each and every day is almost exactly the same.

Wake to clock radio music at 6-am. Rise and shine. Look out over the water behind my condo. Wash my face, comb my hair, get dressed; t-shirt and trousers with socks on my feet. Then down 13 steps to the kitchen and breakfast.

Turn on the coffee maker, look in the freezer and select a frozen breakfast. Today it will be an egg and meat breakfast bowl. Slip it into the microwave for three minutes. While it heats, I look out my kitchen window – nothing new out there. Sun is just starting to brighten the day.

Eat, read the current Kindle book on my tablet, orange juice down, breakfast bowl empty. Still working on my coffee (I take it black – no cream, no sugar). Watch the clock while reading and turning pages.

At 7:45-am I turn off the Kindle and start upstairs to where my computer awaits.

Time to log in for the morning service. We usually come up with a group of 12 or so. Before Covid we used to meet each morning at the Temple minion room, but with current restrictions we each log into a Zoom meeting, each of us seated at our computer or phone.

An hour later, morning prayers completed, I check my investment account, then my e-mail, then Facebook. It was kind of fun when this all started in February of 2020, but it is really getting boring. This usually keeps me going till lunch time – another frozen dinner – stuffed pepper today, Now it's time to check the news – CNN, MSNBC and Fox, I seem to need to know everything that's happening.

After lunch I get to wait for the mail. That gets me outside for a short while when I walk to the mailbox and drop off a bag of trash at the same time.

Back in the kitchen I meander through the mail – trash the advertising, organize the bills and head back upstairs to the computer. More e-mail awaits, some changes in my investments, pay some bills, and explore the news. Eventually, it will be time for dinner which requires making a choice. Looks like it will be chicken fettuccine with broccoli. Zap in the microwave. Pour a glass of wine, and dine alone.

Time for the final hours of this day. Scheduled regular TV programs, no movie tonight; final look at the news; and off to bed after resetting the alarm for tomorrow morning.

And so another day has passed, checked off the calendar. Perhaps I will soon be able to escape this Covid prison and return to normal living.

Bizarre Love Triangle

by Amy Irish

Computer: Oh, plug me in. Connect with me, electric to electric. You are so cold, so empty. Come, caress my keys. Find feeling, meaning, and fleeting heat. Do not leave, do not sleep. I have imagery, I have memes. I can fill your head with characters and scenes. I can give you what you need. No, don't look away—what do you see? The window? With its same birds, their show on repeat? Look here, I have more birds, the most, the best of every color. I have bold pink, sea green. Sleeping, mating, swooping down to feed. Or pure fantasy, CGI beyond real. Birds you've never seen. Oh, keep me open so I can see, so you can see. What else could you need?

Human: I open my computer feeling — let's be honest — hollow. Looking for a show to fill me, or a connection to another human being. But the only people I find online are hiding behind masks of *so-productive, so-fit, so-funny*. And the shows just feel bizarre: people without fear of a virus go to parties, kiss strangers, fall in love. Such complexity and drama can't distract me from all this absence. What do I have left? My eyes wander to the window. There are birds at the feeder, mottled soft-brown and black. Not flashy — simple.

How do they live without constant stories or stimulation? Without a screen or plate of glass always between?

Bird: Greet feeder with feather pirouette. Flap and land above. Grip branch. Chirp: *need to eat need to eat.* Flick higher. Peck bark. Look for danger. Hop and check. Human appears outside. Warble: *freeze freeze.* Blend with tree. Human recedes, watches from a little further. Flit to feeder. Nibble. Crack seeds. Trill the taste: *sweet meats sweet meats.* Swallow. Repeat. Fluff feathers. Feel breeze. Lift and fly. Sing praises to the open sky: *I fly free, I fly free.*

In Lockdown, We Were

by Amy Irish

Yin-Yang rabbits curled together
in the close, earth-scented embrace
of our co-habitation; or tortoises
just carrying on, serenely sheltered
under the domed-skin of solitary shells.

But others grew savage.

There were cougars who hissed and spat
and fought in territorial fury;
kenneled canines, howling
and scratching at walls closing in;
caged birds battering at their bars.

In lockdown, some became beasts

Once again. In their search for a loose
lock, a weak joint, anything
to *oh please* release them back
to their pack, to be pressed body-safe
in the flesh of their flock, their tribe.

In lockdown, in our shared captivity,

We divided. We diverged and unmasked
our animalia.   Unfurled our hidden
inner need for comfort; or caches of food;
or a scurry to safety; or for claws
to sharpen for the long-awaited hunt.

The Most Important Thing
communicating in the time of Corona virus
by Rosemerry Wahtola Trommer

Just two weeks ago, it was sufficient
to say, hello, good morning, good bye.
But now, in every text, every email,
every phone call, I tell my friends
and family how much I love them.
I tell them life is better because
they are in it. I say it with the urgency
of a woman who knows she could die,
who knows this communication could be our last.
I slip bouquets into my voice. I weave love songs
into the spaces between words.
I infuse every letter, every comma, with prayers.
Sometimes it makes me cry, not
out of fear, but because the love is so strong.
How humbling to feel it undiluted,
shining, like rocks in the desert after a rain,
to know love as the most important thing,
to remember this as I keep on living.

The Comeback
by Amy Irish

Dear lovers of language — yes, *you*.
Dear wordsmiths, poets and fictioneers,
historians and humorists. Dear
dictionary checkers. Dear souls
who communicate
carefully, who pause a moment
to craft words, selecting
and releasing them slowly
like passenger pigeons lifting,
feathered and swift, into open air.
Dear journalists and diary-keepers.
Dear lyricists and playwrights.
Dear family of writers, far flung, now united
behind screens and notebooks,
together across all physical barriers—

This is *our* time. To revive
the so-called lost art of letters.
To extend the hand of connection
via mail, both virtual and sealed with a stamp.
To comfort the world but also
to whirl them back to the magic
of words, to reveal our superpowers,

finally displaying our wild hair and fiery eyes
like the wizards we are — yes!
It is time for us to unveil our sorcery
and share our secrets. Time to open
the doors to our cabal, impart to all
the ability to travel any distance,
peek into the past, foretell the future,
dine with those long dead, and embrace
a thousand strange but wondrous
new friends without ever leaving home.

Face-Melting Fury

by Justin Criado

Warning: This short article was written under duress and extreme noise terror.

***Wielded correctly, you can melt* someone's face** with an axe. It's no secret. You don't need the Ark of the Covenant either. It happens all the time, every day, and people love it. Since Robert Johnson sold his soul to the devil down in the Mississippi Delta shortly before War World II, people have been in the face-melting business. Lightnin' Hopkins, Howlin' Wolf and Muddy Waters, along with a long list of blues elder statesmen, laid the foundation by making their respective axes moan and wail. Then you had Jimi Hendrix fornicating with his axe in public, before setting it on fire. Jimmy Page had a double-necked axe. Pete Townshend smashed his axe into a stack of amps. Kerry King and Jeff Hanneman seemingly tortured their axes for their desired effect — hellish squeals and chugging, chainsaw leads. Clearly, there is more than one way to be an axe murderer. If you're still skeptical, watch any of the "The Slumber Party Massacre" movies, which feature much more than just face-melting mayhem.

Having your face melted feels great, especially during live shows. Your jaw goes slack. Your eyes widen. You forget to breathe properly. Your heartbeat quickens. Sometimes a guttural "Yeah!" is accompanied by throwing up the horns. In my case, the white man's overbite and headbanging typically follow. There's something about a shredding guitar that tickles that primordial itch for satisfying vibrations. Solos. Triplets. The Devil's Tritone. Give it all to me.

While cooped up in my basement dwelling, frantically pushing out papers and riding out the cresting wave of a global pandemic, I've become more acquainted with my own axes. Oh, sweet serenaders, how I've neglected you. My acoustic accompanied me here, so I've always plucked away on that, but I recently received my electric axe and amp. It's kind of like riding a bike, though my adult brain, in memorizing more practical, useful bits of info like proper personal finance practices, has forgotten some hard-earned guitar knowledge. Relearning the solos of Queen, Metallica and The Scorpions are on my quarantine to-do list. But I can barely read guitar tabs, let alone sheet music, so I usually learn by ear. Grabbed "100 Classic Blues Guitar Licks" and a Slayer tab book for starters.

The good people of Telluride Music Company are currently looking over an old DigiTech death metal pedal that makes my blues-oriented setup of a 1998 Fender Stratocaster and Hughes & Kettner amp sound like razorblades in a blender. I'm craving that killer crunch. There's a certain amount of emotion that comes from plugging in and thrashing through Slayer's "Raining Blood." When I first heard the intro, especially when those galloping triplets come pummeling through the speakers, my face fell off. Slayer is the soundtrack of the underworld. It's kind of their thing. If the elevator goes south after I expire, I fully expect to hear "Raining Blood" on my way down.

After all the 2020 festivals and concerts I planned to attend were canceled, I started training to melt my own face — a practice that could have serious repercussions, least among them is permanent disfigurement. Down in my dungeon I seethe. I play until my fingers are raw and my forearm cramps. My face distorts, but doesn't melt. I pore over the pages of tabs in an effort to bend certain notes the right way. My right hand is more coordinated than my left. As Lemmy, an all-time face-melter on bass, once said, the left hand makes the shapes, the right hand brings them to life. Abstract analogies don't really help, but they're soothing.

Whether it's music videos, documentaries or concerts, I always look at the guitar players' hands. In the recently released ZZ Top documentary "That Little Ol' Band From Texas," seeing Billy Gibbons play up close is a revelation. He's so smooth and confident, it's as if he's buttering bread.

Like writing, it's all about repetition, including listening to as much music as possible. I need music playing in the background while I write, so I treat it like I'm studying for a double major. Subconsciously, the guitar tones and notes settle into the back of my brain only to resurface when I'm diddling away. Wait a minute that sounds like Amon Amarth. Cue "Guardians of Asgaard." Well, hell, that's it. Then it's time to experiment a little, changing up the rhythm and twisting it to sound fundamentally different than the original version. There's satisfaction in this, but it doesn't necessarily lead to the results I'm looking for.

Without writing a half-baked thesis, this whole face-melting phenomenon is a bit of a conundrum. I'm starting to think it's better when someone else takes their axe to your ears, as there's still a sense of mystery. How did they do that? What tuning are they using? Is that a pedal or some other ungodly effect? Wait for it!

My axes rest in the corner of my living room (I never put them in their cases). I pick them up whenever I'm pacing around wondering what to work on next. Throughout the process of writing this short story, which was undertaken during an uninterrupted stretch of insanity, I picked up my Strat at least a dozen times to blast off a quick tune. A Black Sabbath riff here, and a Mayhem dirge there, even a White Zombie-Slayer-Metallica medley. Motorhead's "Overkill" and Razor's "Executioner's Song" blare while I played. It's sensory overload for sure, but I embrace such auditory chaos. Then it's back to creating this drivel. There are deadlines to hit and papers to publish. Face-melting isn't productive, but it is a nice release.

denning bears

by Erin Robertson

tonight we will sleep
each in our own places
the deep slumber
of denning bears
so warm in our thick black coats
in our cozy hollows
of thick white snow
where no wind stirs
we will dream
calm safe dreams
of honey in unguarded hives
and salmon that jump
into our open mouths
trusting that when winter
eases its grasp
and it's time to
muscle our way
out of the drifts
the sun will be there to warm us

the roots will be ready to nourish us
and our ancestors have already made
clear paths we can follow
to finally drink fresh water
and feel the crisp clean air
settling deep into our lungs
until all our old stale breaths
are wrung right out
yes, you and I,
each in our quiet den,
a mountain or more apart,
we trust implicitly
that there will still be a world
worth waking for
and our cubs will be
just fine

"I am so fortunate! I still have a job. I still work from home, but being required to be alone...."

Just like much of life, work too has changed for many people.

We still plant, we still irrigate, we still reap our crops, yet "work" life shows the ongoing effects of this deadly Covid-19 virus.

Work

Tonight I Pray for All the Doctors, the Nurses, the Healthcare Workers
by Rosemerry Wahtola Trommer

And tonight I think
of the seventeen Italian doctors,
dead. And the hundreds
of thousands of people
whose test results were positive.

And all the doctors, nurses,
health care workers —
some right here in our town.
I think of them eating breakfast,
reading the same discouraging news,
then kissing their loved ones,
putting on their shoes,
and walking out the door,
though resolution's as elusive
as last month's peace —
the peace we didn't
even know we had.

Camp During Covid-19

by Sarah Rutherford

I worked as a summer camp counselor during this international pandemic.

It was not the smartest decision I have ever made in my life. I was exposed to 360 people over the course of eight weeks. Should summer camps have been allowed to open? Maybe not. Should I have willingly worked at one? Probably not. But they did, and I did, and it happened.

I was an unlikely candidate to work at a summer camp, period. I had never attended this particular camp, and I had no plans to do so before the pandemic struck. When my study abroad plans crashed and burned, however, camp became my Plan B. I accepted the job on March 20, 2020, right as the lockdown was getting into full swing. I was not qualified in any way; I didn't know how to fish, tie-dye, or build a fire. But I was desperate for any sort of hope in the turbulence that was the spring of 2020.

When I arrived at camp for staff training in May, it was the first time I had seen someone my own age who was unrelated to me in two months. I went from total isolation with my family to being a part of a pod of thirty young adults at a hundred-acre camp. In the two weeks before the campers arrived, we spent all day with each other. We hugged. We ate indoors. We rejoiced in breaking the rules of the pandemic now that we were a "family unit." A week after arriving, one counselor commented, "This is like the anti-quarantine."

In some ways, it was idyllic. But no summer camp is ever truly an escape from the real world, and this was no exception. We took every camper's temperature every night. We made our campers wear masks to the best of our ability. Sometimes we tried to make it fun by making cow noises and saying it was "MU!" which was short for "Mask Up." Other times we lost our tempers and yelled at the kids to take things seriously. We wiped down balls after each use, we spaced our kids apart at activities, and we instituted drive-through drop-off and pick-up for parents. But despite our best efforts, things went wrong sometimes. When a camper had a fever, they had to be quarantined until their parents arrived, but we couldn't leave a child alone. So, two counselors would sleep on couch cushions on the concrete floor outside the isolation bedroom, dreading the possible outcome.

This fear of an outbreak was always with us. During staff training, we were informed of the protocol that we would use if a camper or staff member tested positive: all children would be required to be picked up within eight hours, and the staff would be quarantined in the main dormitory for two weeks. In one moment, everything could end. We could lose both our jobs and our health in one fell swoop. All of us had chosen this risk, of course, but the anxiety still loomed over camp in the form of whispered news between counselors. *Julie had a fever. She was sent home. Xavier is waiting on his test result. He's quarantined in that building.*

But most of our concern was specific to us. Covid-19 surges and protests felt far away from our isolated existence. When we did have a break, we generally used our precious internet access to communicate with family and friends. Doomscrolling required large amounts of two things we didn't have -- Wi-Fi and time -- so we were prevented from dwelling on negative online news. Unlike many people, we were employed. We were almost never alone, even when we wanted to be. We were also trapped. Due to the possibility of exposure, counselors were not allowed to leave the camp property on their time off, with the exception of a weekly, supervised outing to the nearest town. During this outing, we had our boss' permission to go through a drive-through for fast food and to go to Walmart. That was it. So we ate our fast food in a parking lot and spent our precious free time wandering through every aisle of the local Walmart, relishing in the unlimited cell service and air conditioning. It served as our only glimpse of the outside world. Our perception of the pandemic was shaped by the amount of people wearing masks in Walmart -- not many and the announcements on businesses' signs as we drove past. *Dining room open. Curbside Pickup. Covid-19 Testing Here.*

Camp is hard in the best of times. Lack of sleep, difficult children, and painful sunburns still occurred, regardless of disease. On top of this, we lived under the constant fear of an outbreak affecting both us and our young charges. And yet, camp could also be a place of joy. We had water fights with kids and danced to "YMCA." We played mud gaga. We made banana boats over a campfire. We laughed and cried and fought and made up.

It was eight weeks spent simultaneously in bliss and dread. So how do you reconcile the two? At camp, I struggled with doubting the safety of our operation while also being glad that I was there. I was aware of the consequences of furthering the virus' spread in rural Texas, but I still cherished the chance to have fun with friends. Which was the right response?

I've come to believe there is no good answer to this question. In the end, we did not have any confirmed or suspected Covid-19 cases at our camp. This does not excuse our actions; it simply means that we got lucky. I am grateful for our luck. I also recognize that we put a lot of people at risk. These two statements do not cancel each other out. They exist simultaneously, just like the joy and anxiety with which we lived for eight weeks.

I Still Feel

by Monty Haltiner

Fueled and fired to see this thing through, I inhale a leviathan breath and let out a thank you into the still air. My precautions lay where water and soda normally sit, between the seats of my tired conveyance. Ritualistically I pop the trunk, put my keys in my pocket and lock the doors manually.

Nitrile coated gauntlets I don as I prepare to enter the madness, trying to not leave a mark anywhere, or pick up someone else's careless secretion. I check the dates of packaged beer, making sure everything is fresh and stocked for the masses. Staying clear of the elderly and the absentminded, I shuffle to the isle where sanitizer should be... still empty.

Looking lost, I leave the store and head back to safety. I pop the trunk by hitting the key fob through my trusty denim pants. I touch only the right side of the trunk as I shed my protection and wipe away the potential threats and close it by touching only the left side.

I feel mostly safe as I sit back in my car, but I grab the sanitizer and cleanse my hands and the bottle it came out of. I do this several times a day. I continuously wonder what our nurses and doctors must be going through. I feel unessential but thankful. I feel tired and hopeful. At least I still feel.

Farming in a Pandemic

by Tony Daranyi

It's 4:30 a.m. The quiet darkness is interrupted by the howling and yipping of distant coyotes and the soothing coo of a barn owl. But there's not much else. Except for Vedder, our precious Australian cow dog, who is still sleeping in her bed, curled up. Snoring loudly.

Waking up early allows me to enjoy the peace and quiet of the morning. I read somewhere that it's these hours of the day when the planet is the most still. I believe that. I feel that. This planetary peacefulness is but a few fleeting moments of the day, ones that I grab with all my being to quiet my troubled soul, protecting it from the challenging forces that are consuming us. It's an understatement to say that these are challenging times, not just for myself but for all of humanity. Keeping a positive mental attitude has not been easy.

I immediately head for the stove to turn on the hot water for the first round of morning coffee. The coffee is prepped, religiously, the night before. All that's required in the morning is to pour hot water over fresh grounds into the insulated carafe below.

I go outside for a moment and look for the stars in the night sky. They're beautiful. They twinkle, reminding us of the grandeur of it all. Seeing stars is a positive omen for the day.

It means that smoke isn't filling the sky. At least not right now. Maybe later. But not this morning. The smoke has traveled this summer at various times from all directions: California, Colorado, the Santa Catalina Mountains above Tucson, and Arizona's Kaibab National Forest. Drought is the cause. For all of these fires. Dryness. Tinderbox vegetation. Winds. Heat. Dry lightning. The perfect ingredients for a perfect firestorm.

How are we supposed to think of this smoke? As an unusual occurrence or as something deeper than that? That the West is burning and will continue to burn?

My mind, which was still for a few minutes, now turns, in these dark, early hours of the morning, to climate change. And it's only 5-am for god's sake.

Unlike many of our friends whose lives have been literally uprooted by the virus, our day-to-day farming life hasn't really changed significantly. There's seven of us living at the farm, separated into three different households. We're all focused on the same goal: providing nutritious food for the residents of our regional foodshed, while benefiting the environment. That goal hasn't changed, pandemic or not. What has changed is that we're mostly sheltered in place to provide ourselves a defense against the virus. The Covid-19's presence on the farm would be devastating: we simply have too much life to take care of, with no one else to do it but us. This means no outside farm visitations; customers can pick up orders in a cooler placed at the mouth of the driveway by the road. We've also pivoted our marketing plans away from the farmers market and toward Community Supported Agriculture distributions, and increased commercial accounts to some of our regional food hubs.

The pandemic and climate change are just two of our multiple, onion skin-like layers of anxieties. There's also the economy, there's our supply chain problems due to USPS budget cuts, there's Donald Trump and the rise of fascism in the USA, fomenting a great political divide in our nation. There's income inequality and racism; there's rioting in the streets. There's a serious drought gripping our part of the world, and most of the West.

But, for now, I try to let it all go. It's still dark. It's still peaceful. I go back to my routine: Check out the weather forecast on the computer. Check out sports scores. Check out Snowbrains. Check out my email. Clear out my spam, respond to emails that need attention, trash the rest. Download podcasts that may be worthy of a listen-to later in the day. Then, I turn to the news. Am I ready for the onslaught? Ugh. So much for the peace and quiet. But in these times, it's important to stay informed in order to be vigilant and proactive.

I then move on to my morning yoga and Pilates routine, a lifesaver for the active physical body that seemingly needs to be put back together every morning before the start of the day. This routine, in one form or another, depending on which body part needs attention, has been a part of my life since high school, since the days of playing competitive tennis, taught to me by my tennis coach who was also an advocate of cannabis legalization. Back in the 70s.

I've learned in these dystopian times that the morning routine is vital. It's part of what keeps me balanced, keeps me sane, keeps me from descending into a dark place.

One final check of today's "list of things to do", making sure that nothing important is overlooked, and it's off to the wonder of the outside world. In preparation of today's scheduled watering time, I begin by setting the irrigation valves for the perennials, the lavender field, the fruit trees and shrubs that landscape the farmhouse.

Working outside seems to provide a much-needed attitude adjustment. Perhaps it's the stimulation of all of our senses: the sense of smell, of sound, of taste, of touch, of sight. Perhaps we're lucky as farmers in that we get to exercise our senses every day, all day. I've yet to put on my work boots for the day, but I can already hear the wild birds — the meadowlarks, the red-winged blackbirds, the sparrows — greeting the delicious fresh morning air for the day; I see off in the distance a hint of green in the intensively rotated pasture, a green oasis in a landscape otherwise turned brown by the worsening drought; I can cuddle with our livestock guardian puppies, nearly bowled over by their boundless energy and joy; I can high five Anne's two boys, ages 8 and 6, who are running up the driveway to greet me with their pondering questions of "what are you going to do next?" and "then what are you going to do?" If I'm lucky, I can get a hug out of these incredibly tuned-in young boys.

Chores are next. But the word "chores" implies that it's a repetitive task that's boring, that's forced. I prefer The Three R's, as we call them: rhythm, ritual and routine. That's what this farm thrives on.

The livestock appreciate and thrive on our three Rs. Pigs are fed, layer hens are let out of their homes for the day, turkeys are fed and watered, the goats are pastured, the Livestock Guardian Dogs given their morning meal and moved to another pasture, and then, the most labor-intensive activity of the morning awaits. We rotate, on a daily basis, the 12 pastured poultry pens in the pasture to new locations, giving the pullets fresh green grass to enjoy. They leave behind their manure, which fertilizes the pasture. It's a wonderful cycle, resulting in the healthiest, greenest pasture around.

We're committed to regenerative agricultural practices. We're enhancing bio-diversity, we're building up soil, we're intensively rotating livestock, we're planting trees, shrubs, windbreaks, we're cover cropping, we're taking care of our water resources and working on the hydrology of the farm. This is how we combat the drought. This is how we combat climate change. We want to sequester carbon, we want to utilize water more efficiently, we want, in short, to continue growing food for this amazing regional community that we've nurtured for the past 20 years or so.

Farming this summer, with all the uncertainty that it's presented, has really highlighted for me the need to do the things well that I can control and to let the rest of it all go. Can I control climate change? Really? Can I control the weather and the lack of rain? Can I control Trump's fascist tendencies? Can I change the minds of his cult followers? Can I change the course of the pandemic? Can I bring equality and justice to those victimized by our discriminatory and racist culture? No. I can't.

But I can do the dishes. I can clean the kitchen. I can raise some awesome livestock. I can keep our water resources going. I can fix things. I can love. I can make love. I can garden. I can perform tasks thoroughly. I can stay in good physical shape, climbing mountains, riding hill-climbs on my bike, breathing hard. Those things I can do. Those things keep me sane, keep me from totally losing it.

There's another fallback position that hasn't failed me, and that is, being filled with gratitude. When I'm down and out, feeling depressed, feeling like it's all impossible, feeling like we're swimming upstream to no avail, I reset myself during the day, numerous times if need be, and count my blessings. Not just my blessings. But the blessings that Mother Nature has granted us here on this farm. The beautiful colored skies, the sounds of the birds, the rustling of the leaves, the vibrant sunshine, the crystal clear air (when there's not wildfire smoke!), the ability to breathe. Yes, the ability to breathe and to feel a heartbeat. Over and over and over. The ability to love. To love all. To love one another, to love the animals, the plants, the air and the water. To be thankful. For all of it.

Words with Avery
by Casey Graves

My greatest gift during the crazy year was committing to a nanny position for local friends who just had a baby girl four months prior. After several weeks with my new friend Avery, I began to see the world through the eyes of a child. It was during those days of pure simplicity and joy that I realized that even in the midst of a global pandemic it all comes down to celebrating the little things in life. And with Avery my moments became a celebration of life, love, stillness and smiles from a baby. Here is a poem we wrote together....

Good morning world and how is your day?
We are super excited to get out and play
We have had a nap, a bottle and tummy time
Now we decided to make a rhyme
Bat, hat, rat, sat
A little boy pet a cat
Avery shook her soft rattle
The pretty horse wears a saddle
Soon a walk out in the sun
This is how our day begun

In a time of confusion sometimes all you need is to create a kid's rhyme and hold onto the innocence and wonder from the eyes of a child.

"Travel" has not even been an option for most of us since the pandemic began, and those who have ventured forth have found numerous challenges, along with feelings of anxiety and guilt.

Flying – actually going somewhere during the pandemic via a commercial airline – was a very different kind of activity from the past. Here, you can share in the experience.

Travel

Death & Doom at DIA
by Justin Criado

Flying on a plane during the Covid-19 pandemic is terrifying, let alone idiotic, according to smart people.

In a recent New York Times survey, only seven percent of the 511 epidemiologists polled admitted that they would fly right now.

But I've never claimed to be smart, so I took my chances and experienced the doom-laden dread of cramming myself into a metal bird with other possibly afflicted humans as I flew back to Pittsburgh for my best friend's wedding. As the best man, it's an occasion I wouldn't miss for the world, even though he planned to have me there virtually and postponed the bigger ceremony to next year. If I died enroute, the blood would not be on his hands.

Arriving at the Denver International Airport around 11 p.m. for a 1:30 a.m. redeye to Charlotte, where I had a three-hour layover before heading to the Steel City, I parked about seven miles from the terminal, pissed next to my car and took a deep breath. Then I dove into the maelstrom.

This airport seemed off-kilter. I couldn't find the American Airlines desk or a living person to ask where to go. I wandered aimlessly for what felt like an eternity. My pulse pounded inside my noise-canceling headphones to create a dirge-like drumbeat. Lost. Confused. Irritated. Directionless.

After becoming thoroughly disoriented, I decided to give in. This is purgatory. I must have fallen victim to a violent crash. Somewhere along I-70, I imagined myself drifting in and out of consciousness, this airport being my dying vision.

The south security entrance, which is the one I typically use with the large American flag hanging from the ceiling, had been closed. The north security checkpoint was on the other side, under the gigantic Colorado flag, a friendly TSA employee who noticed my concern told me.

But blank, white walls blocked off a large section of the walkway to the open entrance. Again I walked in circles. After several detours, I found the line. An attractive couple and myself were the only passengers present aside from the TSA skeleton crew. Even the drug-sniffing dogs had the night off.

I asked the lady overseeing the conveyor belt if any airport establishments were open.

"McDonald's."

"Of course there's fast food in the afterlife," I thought. "What about bars? I was thinking I'd get drunk before my flight." A friend who recently traveled by air suggested eating a Xanax beforehand, but another flight-weary comrade said a couple of mini-bottles would have the same effect.

"That much time, huh? No, everything closes down around 6 p.m. ... except McDonald's. You should have been here a month ago, it was like the apocalypse."

Goddammit, I'd have to navigate this post-mortem labyrinth stone sober. At that time, after successfully passing through security, I decided to remove my glasses. And blind.

I found McDonald's at the top of the Terminal A escalator. Ronald McDonald was getting his ass handed to him as a gaggle of my fellow near-dead travelers piled into the four socially distanced lines and a small herd waited off to the side for their orders to be called.

I began to sweat and panicked, "A large sweet tea and two bottles of water ..."

"Anything else?"

"Do you have any alcohol ... for the tea?"

"No."

"OK, that's it."

A lady with arms that ended at her elbows handed me my receipt — Order No. 369 — through the porthole of the protective Plexiglas shield. I began to murmur the song of the same name.

"3, 6, 9

The goose drank wine

The monkey chewed tobacco on the streetcar line

The line broke, the monkey got choked

And they all went to heaven in a little rowboat."

Oh, sweet insanity, you cruel jokester. I grabbed my liquid and scurried to find a spot at my gate. Landing in a seat facing the window overlooking the airport apron behind a large pillar, I tore off my facemask and quickly consumed all my drinks. A lady nearby stared in horror as dribble fell from my chin and onto my chest. I returned the glare, as if to say, "Mind your own funeral."

As a metal mix played through my headphones, I sat there, blind, reading "The Collected Schizophrenias" by Esmé Weijun Wang, which is a collection of powerful essays about the author's life with mental illness, but it did nothing to assuage my anxiety. I checked my news app, "BREAKING: UFOS OVER WISCONSIN?" Finally.

I began to write in my Moleskin. In checking my notes from that fearful night in preparing this piece, I can barely discern my scrawls. In no particular order:

Ignore the other humans enjoying their McDonald's as if it's their last meal.

If you're gonna die, die with a Big Mac in your belly.

'The weirdo in the corner won't stop writing,' I hear them whisper. 'I'll die if I do!' I scream back.

DIA (Denver International Airport) is eerily similar to DOA (Dead On Arrival).

Once aboard the initial flight, I passed out before we took off, then slept-walked until arriving in Pittsburgh, where a friend picked me up. We immediately headed to Primanti Brothers for oversized sandwiches and Iron City beer.

All hysterics aside, I'd gladly relive the fear-induced fever dream as Darin and Maggie officially married in front of a small group of family and friends during a quaint ceremony in downtown Pittsburgh. Congratulations, Lyles.

Visiting with the Animals
by Warren Roy

It was Wednesday, early morning and I was going outside – not for just a quick daily trip to the mailbox – but a real outdoors adventure to the zoo. It's been more than six months since my last outdoors pleasure trip, and I am ready!

Doorbell rings. She is here. I put on my jacket, grab a bottle of water from the fridge, pick up two masks from the table, and head out to the car and off we go!

Easy parking today, just a few cars today and we were able to park close to the entry. No line here. We headed down the clearly marked trail – footprints on the cement about six-feet apart – and on to the animals. We spent about three hours wandering past and gazing, and sometimes gaping, at the animals. It was wonderful.

We did have a camera and did shoot some memories. Of course, no visitor facilities were open so we could not stop for a quick ice cream or coffee break.

The lack of crowds was both terrific and sad. Yes, we had easy viewing watching the giraffes reach high for their snacks... and the gorilla dining on his selection of fresh fruit. But the important thing was we were out in the open, enjoying the fresh air, the green surroundings. The quiet, the lack of crowds, and just being outdoors and away from my prison. Outdoors!

This zebra just kept looking around for some grass to nibble on.

A Colorado Mother's California Snapshot

by Kierstin B. Bridger

This is the land of Land of the Lost
Dinosaur-size plants and succulents so big
they could eat you.
Candy striped Amaryllis grows
not in Christmas time crocks
but wild in yards
though not as bright as the LED lights
which dot dorm room windows—
It's the college part of town
where the cool spring wind
is rife with pot and laundry detergent
and competing taco shops can tell you
where the freshman feast.

I came out to make sure my daughter
and her dog got enough care.
Wisdom teeth gone and all that lingers
is what smarts — opioids
unable to touch the pain in her jaw.
Walking side streets I see
all the kids are masked
even on their skateboards --
a few garages yawn with skinny boys
flexing inside, pumping iron to get hard

I'm in a parade of palm trees and sweatshirts
snippets of conversation coast by
"like in person, in person?"

I'm invisible in this oncoming dusk
when the appearance of a fingernail moon reminds
me we were going to do pedicures tonight
but instead I find myself on the corner
of Dorothy and Debbie
an intersection that makes me laugh
then think of my girl laying on the couch,
her pup curled like a doughnut on her belly,
ice pack near her chin.
How much more laundry will I fold before I go home?
Hoping tomorrow I can take her for a drive,
watch the waves wash into shore
but that may not happen.
I might just have to hold her hair
as she spits and rinses on repeat again.

CRUISING
by Richard Vizzier

My wife Bev and I were the 2nd and 3rd confirmed Covid-19 cases in Virginia. We caught it on a Nile River cruise in February, 2020. She actually got much sicker than me, even though I am 68 and she is 59. It is one random virus....

My wife Bev and I enjoy traveling. There was a great promotion for a Nile River cruise and we jumped on it. February is a perfect time to visit Egypt with the temperatures ranging in the mid-80s. News regarding the virus was starting to break, so the week before I looked up Egypt's infections and there was only one reported case in over 95 million people. So, it was a go.

The first few days we visited Cairo and the surrounding Egyptian artifacts. Then we flew down to the Ethiopian and Egyptian border to embark on our vessel, the MS A'Sara. The vessel held about 120 passengers, with roughly half from Europe and half from the USA. It was a wonderful cruise, very educational and also relaxing. The last day of being onboard many of us felt like we were coming down with upper respiratory issues. We returned to Cairo for one last night, flying out to the USA the next day.

On March 5th we flew out of Cairo to Istanbul, then onward to Dulles Airport on Turkish Airlines. After a very long trip we arrived in Dulles around 6-pm. On the way back, Bev was getting very sick and had a fever. Thankfully, we cleared customs quickly and went to our hotel at Dulles. Bev was not interested in eating, but I did grab a bite. We went to bed very early. Friday morning, March 6th we got up, checked out, and drove straight for home. We did not eat breakfast or stop for gas, just drove straight down. Around Richmond Bev said, "you need to take me to a hospital because I feel terrible." We decided to go to Sentara Leigh because it was fairly close. We got there around 11-am. It was raining, so I let Bev out at the Emergency Room entrance and I parked the car.

Upon arriving at the hospital, Bev informed the nurse that we just returned from a trip to Egypt. They immediately took her temperature, which was 102, then escorted Bev to a private room. When I entered her room they were prepping her for an IV, having determined that she was dehydrated. They tested her for the flu, the result came back negative.

A little after noon I received an e-mail from Gate One, our cruise company, that we had been exposed to Covid-19. I left the room to show the e-mail to the ER doctor and he told me to get back into the room immediately. I asked him if we could use the bathroom, as we had not used a restroom facility since we left the hotel over six hours earlier. They finally brought us in a portable toilet. I asked if I could leave the room and was told if I left the room I would be arrested. Medical staff came back in and took me to another room, stating that they were going to admit me as well.

I had a low-grade fever, a headache, and a scratchy throat, but did not feel that ill. I kept asking questions about what was going to happen to us, but got no answer. Around 2pm, I was doing searches on my iPhone regarding Covid and found out the Virginia Department of Health (VDH) was the lead. I found a number for the Virginia Beach extension and called it; it was busy. After about 10 tries it finally rang, but after the eighth ring it went to voice mail.

I left a detailed voicemail with our names, email address, phone numbers, that we were in Sentara Leigh, and that we had been exposed to Covid. I told them that I could send them the email. I never heard back. Right before 5-pm the ER doctor came into my room. He was not happy and asked me if I had called VDH. I said yes. He then gave me a choice of staying in the hospital, explaining that it would probably be five days until we were tested, or go home. I didn't know Bev had already said she wanted to go home, but when he told me that I said we were going home. They gave us some masks and gloves and told us we were to self-isolate.

I stopped by a Walgreens to get Tylenol and Ibuprofen, and a thermometer. People looked at me like I was from outer space since I was wearing a mask and gloves. We went home and crashed.

The next day, Saturday, March 7th, we both felt like we had been run over by a truck. We slept in different spaces. Food tasted horrible to both of us. Even with Tylenol and Ibuprofen, Bev was running a fever over 101 and she was developing a bad cough. Sunday, around noon, we got a call from Sentara Princess Anne saying that they had test kits and asking if we could come to the Emergency Room. They told us to call a specific number when we arrived and they would walk us in. We got there around 2PM and they put us in PPE and escorted each of us to separate rooms. They did both throat and nasal swabs, and shortly thereafter sent us home. On Tuesday we got a call (actually a conference call with a number of Doctors and Health Officials on the line) confirming that we did have Covid-19. They asked how we were doing and we described our symptoms. They said if we turned worse we would need to go to Sentara Princess Anne and gave us a number to call. They also wanted the names of our personal doctors and had them call us daily.

On Wednesday, during Bev's call with her doctor, she heard Bev cough and said, that is not good and called in an antibiotic and cough medicine with codeine. After about two days on the medications, Bev's condition starting improving. We got an email questionnaire twice daily from VDH asking us to record our temperatures.

Family and friends were bringing us food and leaving it at the door for us. After 6 straight days without a fever or significant symptoms, we got clearance from VDH that we could stop isolating.... about the same time that everything around us was starting to close.....

We found out that over 50 of the Americans on our trip came down with Covid from the cruise.

Since then both Bev and I have donated Covid Plasma. Bev's went to a hospital in Richmond, Virginia and mine went to a hospital in Charleston, West Virginia.

Since no one really understood the virus when we had it, we weren't afraid. Bev, who is younger, and has none of the risk factors, got much sicker than I did. It was definitely a learning experience for us.

Rising in Phoenix
by Kierstin B Bridger

I'm worried the plane won't take off
too heavy with the burdens
of Covid time.
The woman in back of me lost
three members of her family
"I still feel married," she says,
"will for a long time."

The woman I side-eyed for allowing
her mask to dip below her nose
has her hands full with a boy who interrupts
the quiet with his piercing voice, a boy who
may not be capable of complying with the mask order.
In fact, I spy him self-soothing, rocking, repeating
words, readjusting his seat.

Across the aisle the flight attendant engages
with his grandmother who did little britches rodeo,
who did barrels too, they both have that in common.
Behind me an eighty-year-old man assures his seat mate
he's been shot with both doses of the vaccine
"so many friends never got the chance," he says to the
widow.

Such sad eyes pass me on their way to the back

All of us beaked and breathing our own stale breath
and then, belts fastened we taxi out into the desert air —
turns out we're flying, turns out the boy has saved us all
it is his voice that lifts us with a song,
a melody I've never heard but its arcing timbre
has tamed my nerves, stilled the bantam panic
has breathed fresh wind under these leaden wings.

Sequestering
by Art Goodtimes

For those of us who grew
accustomed
to the tarantella of modern life
in pre-Covid America
getting time away was luxury

People paid fortunes
that could have bankrolled
a homeless shelter
months
Taking junkets
Honeymoons. Private
retreats. Living the high life
Or indulging hermit
fantasies
we couldn't get enough of

Just as now
we can't wait to escape
the tyranny of the unvaccinated
fear that holds us
rebels
in lockdown

Like so many of the immigrants
Lady Liberty welcomes to our shores
& then Big Donald Warbucks
                    shuns or has shot
Won't let over the fence

Hiding
        as so many of us are
from everything
not to do with ourselves

Even the "holidays" were affected by the pandemic.
It was still a happy time, but it sure did have its differences.

New Years Day came and went,
but Covid made it different . . . very different.

Everyone approached the turning of the calendar year
in their own way, and you will find out how some felt about it
in the following section.

Holidays

Age of Covid
Anonymous

T'was the month of Christmas
And all through the town
People wore masks
That covered their frown.

The frown had begun
Way back in the Spring
When a global pandemic
Changed everything.

They called it Corona
But unlike the beer
It didn't bring good times
It didn't bring cheer.

Contagious and deadly
This virus spread fast
Like a wildfire that starts
When fueled by gas.

Airplanes were grounded
Travel was banned
Borders were closed
Across air, sea and land.

As the world entered lockdown
To flatten the curve
The economy halted
And folks lost their verve.

From March to July
We rode the first wave
People stayed home
They tried to behave.

When summer emerged
The lockdown was lifted
But away from caution
Many folks drifted.

Now it's November
And cases are spiking
Wave two has arrived
Much to our disliking.

Frontline workers
Doctors and nurses
Try to save people
From riding in hearses.

It's true that this year
Has had sadness a plenty
We'll never forget
The year 2020.

And just 'round the corner
The holiday season
But why be merry?
Is there even one reason?

To decorate the house
And put up the tree
When no one will see it
No-one but me.

But outside my window
The snow gently falls
And I think to myself
Let's deck the halls!

So, I gather the ribbon,
The garland and bows
As I play those old carols
My happiness grows.

Christmas ain't cancelled
And neither is hope
If we lean on each other
I know we can cope.

New Year's 2020 – 2021

by Colette DeVito

Those of you that know me well know I hate New Year's.... I don't know why, I just always have. Not this year..... this hands down has been the hardest, most horrible year of my life. I thought 2013 was bad, but 2020 came roaring in and obliterated 2013. So yes, it can always get worse. That being said, I sit this morning and reflect. Someone asked me what was the best thing that happened to me in 2020. I looked at that person like they had six heads. My immediate response was nothing, nothing good happened in 2020. So today, I reflect, because 2020 definitely left scars, scars that will never go away. But I hope that in 2021, I can minimize the appearance of the scars. I sit here and I'm going to try to accentuate the positive.

Education: The quarantine shit-show. Nuff said, but the positive that came out of that is I definitely appreciate educators more than I ever did, and I had a decent appreciation to begin with. This definitely left a scar on me, I know I joke about some stuff, but I do truly have PTSD when it comes to schooling. I am not a person who is cut out for education. I'd be the worst teacher on the planet. I definitely do not have what it takes — I own that. Just know that when I don't agree with things the school district does, it doesn't mean I don't appreciate them, I do, more than they will ever know.

Health: I'm grateful my family is healthy, only one family member (that I'm aware of, anyway) caught Covid-19 and thankfully it was a very mild case. Mentally, Covid did a number on me. I pray that in 2021 I can turn it around. I'm not going to lie, I'm truly terrified I won't be able to. I have become complacent, not because I've become lazy, but because I've been beaten down. There are things I don't follow through with as a parent, as a wife, as a friend, as an employee and as a person. I just don't have it in me right now to fight, I'm mentally exhausted, and there's no fight left right now. I need to fix that in 2021. I hope I can. I have some issues I need to work on with my physical health. I need to get to the bottom of these facial symptoms and get my overall self together, and get back to working on my vitamin levels.

Family and friends: My family and I have drifted apart and if I were to be honest, it was before Covid-19. However, Covid has brought new friends to me and really shown me who my true friends are..... so while I am sad about the family, I'm thankful for all my friends. In some cases, they were TRUE lifesavers. I'm going to concentrate on solidifying these friendships, and work on my family relationships.

So, good things did happen in 2020, including reading over 1000 books (I love to read) and I actually have several books written in my head, but that's a whole other creature. My oldest child moved close to me and brought along his woman-friend, and one of my "kids" is adopting two children, essentially making me a pseudo grandma. I'm not naive and I know the ball isn't going to drop tonight and, poof, everything will be better. I know part (hopefully) of 2021 is going to suck, but I do truly see it getting better, I hope by the summer.

I have to be honest and say more bad than good occurred in 2020 and it will definitely go down as the worst year ever for me, but I'm going to try to take the few positives I've garnered and try to fix me in 2021. It will be an uphill battle, but then anything that's worth it is always hard.

I love you my family, my friends, and I truly am grateful for all I do have. I know I fell off that wagon from time to time this year and it seemed at times that I didn't appreciate what I had, but that's just not the case. That was me trying to right myself (not successfully in some cases) but know it was actually the opposite, I became more grateful and appreciative.

So, Happy New Year my family and friends, I truly hope 2021 is better for all. I wish nothing but the best for everyone, and health, wealth, and happiness to all. XOXO

Twelve Days of COVID

by Kerri Pastrano

(sing to the tune of Twelve Days of Christmas)

On the first day of Covid my true love gave to me:
a month-long sh!#tty lockdown.

On the second day of Covid my true love gave to me:
2 new streaming services
and a month-long sh!#tty lockdown.

On the third day of Covid my true love gave to me:
3 bars of soap
2 new streaming services
and a month-long sh!#tty lockdown.

On the fourth day of Covid my true love gave to me:
4 boring zoom meetings
3 bars of soap
2 new streaming services
and a month-long sh!#tty lockdown.

On the fifth day of Covid my true love gave to me:
5 rolls of toilet paper
4 boring zoom meetings
3 bars of soap
2 new streaming services

and a month-long sh!#tty lockdown.

On the sixth day of Covid my true love gave to me:
6 boxes of gloves
5 rolls of toilet paper
4 boring zoom meetings
3 bars of soap
2 new streaming services
and a month-long sh!#tty lockdown.

On the seventh day of Covid my true love gave to me:
7 reusable face coverings
6 boxes of gloves
5 rolls of toilet paper
4 boring zoom meetings
3 bars of soap
2 new streaming services
and a month-long sh!#tty lockdown.

On the eighth day of Covid my true love gave to me:
8 containers of hand sanitizer
7 reusable face coverings
6 boxes of gloves
5 rolls of toilet paper
4 boring zoom meetings
3 bars of soap
2 new streaming services

and a month-long sh!#tty lockdown.

On the ninth day of Covid my true love gave to me:
9 paperback books
8 containers of hand sanitizer
7 reusable face coverings
6 boxes of gloves
5 rolls of toilet paper
4 boring zoom meetings
3 bars of soap
2 new streaming services
and a month-long sh!#tty lockdown.

On the tenth day of Covid my true love gave to me:
10 jigsaw puzzles
9 paperback books
8 containers of hand sanitizer
7 reusable face coverings
6 boxes of gloves
5 rolls of toilet paper
4 boring zoom meetings
3 bars of soap
2 new streaming services
and a month-long sh!#tty lockdown.

On the eleventh day of Covid my true love gave to me:
11 pairs of stretch pants

10 jigsaw puzzles
9 paperback books
8 containers of hand sanitizer
7 reusable face coverings
6 boxes of gloves
5 rolls of toilet paper
4 boring zoom meetings
3 bars of soap
2 new streaming services
and a month-long sh!#tty lockdown.

On the twelfth day of Covid my true love gave to me:
12 bottles of wine
11 pairs of stretch pants
10 jigsaw puzzles
9 paperback books
8 containers of hand sanitizer
7 reusable face coverings
6 boxes of gloves
5 rolls of toilet paper
4 boring zoom meetings
3 bars of soap
2 new streaming services
and a month-long sh!#tty lockdown.

A Christmas Call

by Mayela Calabria Harris

Last month and the month before, I read aloud my first "book" to my mother and sister during weekly Zoom calls. I felt compelled to write another story so we could immerse ourselves in a healthy amount of distraction, yet again as we celebrate our first Christmas together over the phone.

You know, much like in Victorian times when people regaled one another with songs, storytelling, music, dancing, and feasts. Yeah, just like that, I dreamingly imagined! Before I type any further, I will insert an adult content warning here, as no less than a few sentences in and I feel like cursing. Bull shit! What the hell kind of #!@!%$ Christmas is this? Zoom Christmas. Are you kidding me?

Thank you for allowing me the opportunity to vent and let me segue into allowing me to also introduce my two new housemates at this time, whom you may also know — Mrs. Anxiety and Mr. Anger. These uninvited houseguests have been visiting since on or around March 24. I remember their arrival as it coincided with the day my husband contracted Covid-19. This unhappy couple has been hanging around ever since despite my hinting that they have overstayed their welcome both at my former home and the new "old" one we moved into.

They are inescapable and unbelievable. They sleep in my bed, wake me up at night, take up hours of the day at times, mess with my memory, and Mr. Anger even caused me a speeding ticket, and the list goes on. They could take over the content of this story if I let them. That is how invasive they are.

Case in point, Mrs. Anxiety subsequently came with me to the courthouse where I had to address the 90-mph questionable blip in my history the district attorney politely indicated to me when he said, "this does not match your history." Yeah, no shit, Sherlock; Mr. Anger said in my head, but you try driving the highway these days where some of the good citizens of our state have learned that there are fewer troopers on the road and therefore feel they can drive Mario Andretti style or with total disregard of the law.

Hold the phone, you must be saying. You just admitted to driving 90-mph yourself. In my defense, and it is a shameful and thin one. I reached that level of speed, totally unbeknownst to me as Mr. Anger was shouting so loudly in my head that I never even realized I was driving that fast since I was forced to accelerate to that speed briefly to narrowly change lanes as Mr. Redneck in the truck driving erratically and slowly in the passing lane in front of me for God knows I can't remember how many miles, decided to floor it when I attempted to pass him from the slow lane.

You see he refused to move out of the passing lane and give up his lead dog status, a status so prestigious it boggles the mind. So, yeah, it was floor it and move over or rear end the minivan that was quickly coming into view in that split second decision. And, as you can imagine, just my luck a trooper was watching from an overpass while I acted stupidly. But I can't seem to find any of those troopers in my many daily travels white knuckling the steering wheel while two cars drive weaving in and out of traffic at speeds so fast you can feel your own vehicle shimmy a little as they pass from the wind off their cars. It has happened so frequently since the pandemic that I keep wondering, are these the same two speedsters following me or multiple pairs of speed demons? And why did the trooper only pull me over when the driver I had to overtake was speeding too?

As I type these words, I realize how much I am now struggling to put onto paper what has become of my life and of ourselves. But telling the story, typing the story, and sharing the story is perhaps the strongest stance to take against them and it. Doctor, heal thyself. I know, I know. As a clinician I can understand and clearly see all of what is happening to me and to others. I have learned to adapt, zig and zag as the situations allow, train for the marathon, steer clear of danger and adjust my sails. Problem is, despite knowing how to cope, having the skills to do so, and sometimes even the energy to show others how, as I counsel my clients or encourage a family member or friend, I am TIRED!

Last summer I made another mistake in partaking in an amusement ride called the Thrasher which I regret wholeheartedly and all I could think of aside from wishing for an immediate death to put me out of my misery was also, "I want to get off this ride... how much longer... I can't stand this anymore." Point in fact, here I am again in another regrettable situation with all the same emotions, but this time I am not alone. Thankfully, the ride which involved thrashing my flailing body parts in a rhythmic and repetitive pattern for at least five minutes in opposing directions and bouncing my relatively small and delicate brain off every interior lining of my skull came to an end. This too shall pass. I know, I know. But where is the consolation in all this? Zoom Christmas, Zoom Christmas call, Bah humbug!

And yet... A Christmas call is still a call that I am lucky enough to take and make and participate in. I have family to celebrate Christmas with. I will likely have a special dinner to eat for Christmas. I have a home with a tree lit inside and lights on the outside. I have a husband who survived Covid-19 once and still fights it off almost every day he goes to work. Mind you, his sense of smell and taste have not returned fully and there are no ornaments on our tree this year as I could not quite muster the level of cheer and energy to unpack them and adorn all those tree branches.

But the threat of Covid has taught me to live in the moment even more because it is a fabulous excuse to use to enjoy something now rather than later. I already opened and re-wrapped my Christmas gift from my husband who reminded me that he did not want me to get Covid and die, so I should open my present now. Morbid logic I know, but I willingly agreed and do not regret my decision one iota.

One could surmise, based on the gift I unwrapped, that my husband really loves me, but I know that already, minus the bling. I am not a total Barbarian, as I imagine you are thinking. I do actually put on real clothes every once in a while, long before the funk of my sweatpants forces me to... and, I did put the present under the tree again to open at the appropriate time on Christmas day... again.

As I was saying, Christmas dinner with family is planned, but outdoors. And with only two cousins, rather than the usual gaggle of family for everyone's safety and likely in a pouring rain according to the forecast and yet... And yet my brother recently contracted the corona virus around the same time as his wife.

What kind of Christmas memories will they take away from this year? And their four children? And my mother, with whom my sister and I will be having the afore mentioned Zoom Christmas call, who was most likely looking forward to a fabulous Christmas meal after months of eating what she not so politely describes as being beyond unpalatable, but much more politely than with the words you all know I would have used. A meal that would have been lovingly prepared by my brother if not for Covid. She will have to endure yet another hardship of many as she remains jailed in a senior housing community without his healthy dose of Italian love in portions better and bigger than any visions of sugar plums.

She should have been enjoying "fattening the curve", rather than flattening the curve, much like I am steadily practicing every time I lift a weighted spoon of chocolate chip cookie dough out of a gallon of ice cream or from an uncooked package the Pillsbury Dough Boy taunts me with. And yet, she is the sole survivor of the parents in my husband's and my family as my father joins us at Christmas only in spirit and Stephen's parents are this year both notably absent for the holiday.

I mailed my Christmas cards old-school style this year with a heavy heart, not only because their names were absent from my list, but because Christmas is different this year. Gone was the pressure to get these cards done, instead sadly replaced with, "what the hell am I supposed to write inside these cards this year?" Thank God, I had a stash of blank ones, as the prewritten Hallmark gooey narrative of "have the merriest of all seasons" or whatever standard level of cheeriness just didn't feel true let alone appropriate to send this go around. But it pained me to write the truth rather than send the pre-scripted verse and wishes. And yet... And yet, I hope that every family member and friend I lovingly thought of and mailed a card to might have had the tiniest sliver of joy in receiving my love despite the toned-down wishes.

My beloved dog Peachy, we learned, had a mast cell tumor a couple of months ago. And we were blessed with the selling of our home to be in a financial position to spare no expense in tackling her cancer that we could not have afforded literally two months before. She underwent surgery and the doctors told us she was recovering nicely and they feel good about the margins and what they were able to remove.

And thirty minutes later, they called back with different news. "She is having pulmonary issues and let's rule out... blah, blah, blah" because I could not really hear or comprehend anything they said after a few words into the second call. There it is again. The inevitable shoe drop. I have desperately tried to live a life without worrying about when the other shoe will drop but much like a dog in a Pavlovian experiment, if the behavior is repeatedly reinforced, it is hard to behave or think any other way. "Your dog has a pulmonary embolism, she has significant heart disease... advanced heart disease... prognosis of a week or maybe a year, blah, blah, blah."

And yet, two months later Peachy is peppy, fully recovered from the surgery so that whatever time she has left, we have given her quality of life again, playfulness, comfort, and joy. Her joy is our joy. I can still be joyful despite knowing what I know, lacking total control and fearing the unknown. I can be at peace because I did all I could, even though it will not be enough to save her. I did everything I could. She is more loved and spoiled because we are running out of time and she deserves more than I can possibly repay her.

I still want a merry Christmas. I still want to be grateful for all my blessings. I really, really, really want peace on Earth this year especially. Peace on Earth this year. Earth this year. Earth seemed so different as it seemed to shrink in size, recoil in response to our mistreatment of her. I believe Mother Nature stepped in as any protective mother would to lash out at all the abuse our beloved planet has seen and to perhaps take matters into her own hands by culling the population with a virus to teach us a lesson. And yet. And yet, some people still don't see the writing on the wall.

Some people were altogether blind this year, some people were conned and didn't even know it. Still don't know it. And yet. And yet some people found their voices and stood up. Some people rose and some people fell. A lot of people rose, but a lot of people are still falling. Can you hear them calling? Can you hear them shouting? Can you hear them at all? I can. I can hear more clearly now than perhaps in some time.

I don't like a lot of what I am hearing, feeling or seeing, but as I once said to a dear friend who was knee deep in the struggles of cancer she has since survived, I reminded her that she may not like all of what is happening to her, or even control much of it, but that she was not alone and she was being heard by me. I quoted the movie Avatar to her… I see you. My sister recently and similarly quoted back to me that she could hear the ring in the Lladro bell I gave her this Christmas, the gift I made her open early, which was missing the ball to make it ring like the theme in the movie the Polar Express. My sister tapped into her childhood strengths and beliefs to let me know she felt my love. She felt the true meaning of Christmas in my small gift of love during that Christmas call. And isn't that what Christmas is all about Charlie Brown?

Extinction Journals

by Justin Criado

In March, 2020 when society crumbled under the weight of the virus, I began an "extinction" journal to chronicle the external and internal insanity of this plague-stricken year. Three Moleskins and counting later, I've been rereading my musings.

Thursday, March 19, 2020

I don't mind too much if this is the new normal. People are being nicer and kinder to one another. Pollution has decreased, too. Maybe Mother Nature knows what's best for her and us.

Work has been crazy since Thursday, March 12, after the virus took over the nation. We're doing important work, though. These are unprecedented times. It's kind of exciting covering the end of the world. Strangely, I'm feeling more inspired then I have in a while. Think this is going to produce some good work. Hard to take my mind off it. Getting high and letting the mind wander helps.

Thursday, March 26, 2020

I'm high. Just sent my Sunday story to (Associate Editor Suzanne Cheavens) and smoked a bowl. Now I'm watching a

Pink Floyd documentary. It's such a stoner thing to do, but I love Pink Floyd. Have you ever listened to "Wish You Were Here," "Dark Side of the Moon," "The Wall" or "The Division Bell?" I mean, damn. It's immortal music. It's in the bones. Damn, I dig Pink Floyd. I'll fight you to the death about their greatness. Trippy, blues-based rock turned psychedelia. But I think you need to be stoned to fully, properly, enjoy them.

What mad geniuses they all were. How lucky we are to be able to listen to and enjoy it. Same with Black Sabbath. All geniuses. They literally created a new sound that spawned a new musical genre — heavy metal — that spawned seemingly countless subgenres. Without Black Sabbath you don't have the New Wave of British Metal, thrash, hardcore, death metal, black metal (first and second wave), the New Wave of American Heavy Metal, grindcore, metalcore, Swedish death metal, groove metal, sludge, doom/stoner metal, nu metal and so on. It can all be traced back to Black Sabbath.

It's crazy how much of an impact they've had on alternative music and how recently it all happened. Like, my dad is older than heavy metal. He also loves Pink Floyd and Black Sabbath, so I remember listening to both bands growing up. We both agree that Floyd's best work was the "Dark Side of the Moon" to "Animals" era of the 1970s. He even admitted he wasn't the biggest fan of "The Wall," which he called "poppy." We also both agree that the best way to listen to Pink

Floyd is stoned. Give it a try if you've never done it and you'll get it. If you don't, then I truly feel sorry for you.

Wednesday. April 1, 2020

There are six new cases in the county — seven total now. None of them are serious as all seven people self-isolated and are recovering "well," as officials put it.

Still haven't left the house. I'm used to it. Having a mini-gout flare up, which is always annoying. Luckily, I don't have to go anywhere. Called in a new prescription, too. My diet and exercise routine has been messed up by this shit. I'm not really exercising at all, and I'm snacking more since I'm stuck inside. Gotta change it up. It's too easy to be lazy.

Was supposed to fly to Iceland today. Obviously, that trip got canceled. It's a bummer. Karlee (my sister) and I were so excited about it, our first time in Europe. This year seems to be a loss already. Just delay everything a year basically. This pandemic is insane, but one day we'll look back and make fun of how unbelievable it all was. We can all say we lived through history. It's not that exciting.

Monday, May 25, 2020

Called Grandma today. Haven't talked to her in a while, so it was nice catching up. She's doing well, for the most part. She told me some of my great ancestors, including my great-

great-grandmother, died during the 1918 Spanish flu pandemic after moving to Pennsylvania from Scotland. She said they're all buried in DuBois, Pennsylvania, in a cemetery she hasn't been to since she was little. Would like to go back there with her, but who knows when we'll be able to travel.

Saturday July 4, 2020

Fourth of July didn't feel the same. With the pandemic and general disarray of the country, I really didn't care to celebrate. Got up early and hiked up Bear Creak to the Wasatch trailhead. There was some weather, so I hiked down quickly.

Wednesday, Sept. 2, 2020

The end of the world is taking longer than I expected. Humanity, particularly here in America, has had enough time to embarrass itself over and over again. Each century humans are doomed to repeat the errors of the past. When will new generations learn and break the patterns of our parents?

Saturday, Oct. 31, 2020

Is 2020 actually happening or did the Earth slip away from the Sun's gravitational pull and drift into the cold death of space and everyone is trapped in a cosmic coma nightmare?

Wednesday, Nov. 25, 2020

I turned 30 today. Every time I say it out loud it burns my throat like a shot of cheap whiskey. But I can't say I resent it.

Some burns are more familiar than others, and the big 3-0 feels right. It's time to settle into the slow thrum of life. Nobody's interested in the melodramatic nocturnal activities of a 30-year-old with a burly beard, bald spot, bad eyes and bum knees. Act your age, they say. But no one knows how to act during this pandemic.

Thanksgiving is this week and the people in charge are telling everyone to stay put, don't travel, don't interact with out-of-town family and friends or strangers, for that matter. There is going to be a spike of cases. The hospitals will be overrun, and the terminally ill will be forced to lay down and die in the streets.

The virus doesn't take holidays off. But neither do the brave frontline health care workers. Their reality is different than all of ours. Keep it in mind the next time you're feeling bad about your age or not being able to vacation outside of the canyon. Be thankful, you old goat.

Thursday, Dec. 31, 2020

It's the last day of this Godforsaken year. It's 7:30 p.m. and "Willy Wonka & the Chocolate Factory" just came on. I'm lying on my couch. My one-eyed black cat Ripley is sleeping at my feet. I decided not to celebrate such trivial turns of time years ago. I used to go out, spend too much money on booze and revel amongst the stupefied crowds whenever the clock struck midnight. Not this year. All the bars in town are closed right now under a state order anyway.

2021, I suspect, will start just as 2020 ended, with social distancing and virus-centric public health ordinances. Problems don't magically disappear with the passing of time. You gotta work for it. There are no secrets or supernatural solutions to progress.

Augustus Gloop is drowning in a chocolate milk river. Too much of a good thing can kill you, yah know. I'm listening to the people in the condo above me rampage and riot as if tomorrow will bring them some unexpected fame and fortune. Their good time reminds me of a Bukowski poem.

"New Year's Eve always terrifies me. Life knows nothing of years."

"Solstice"

by Monty Haltiner

Again. It's happening, again. I wake to a familiar sensation. A weakness that has hobbled my breathing washes over my once vigorous body. I want to, I need to, but I can't rise. This helpless sensation has infected my spirit too.

Today is the start of what is normally one of the best weeks of the year, Christmas week. Today is the shortest day of the year, or rather the day with the least amount of the life-giving sun. I want to head outside and seek its warming rays, hike into the hills and feed on Mother Nature's energy, but I lay in bed, frozen.

I have work to do, errands to run, presents to buy, meals to cook and all I do is lie in bed, lazy and listless. Frustration builds.

Trapped in my own lethargy, my mind wanders to why people I know, friends and family, deny what is happening. Selfishness? Laziness? Political partisanship? It's been around nine months since Covid made its way to the United States and two months since I came down with it and recovered. Yes, it was only a more virulent version of being sick to me. Yes, many people don't even get sick, but some people die. I know everyone will meet their maker and that our lives on this planet are short and nothing is guaranteed. I just can't comprehend how people care so little for those around them, let alone themselves. Maybe they are more tired of humanity than is bearable. I just don't understand.

Two hours have passed since I woke. I am still in a fog. I could've done so much with those two hours. I feel a desire to start some new habits, to help break me out of the hold of this lingering Covid fatigue. I've felt like that for weeks now, but have not mustered the energy to make it happen. I need some small victories. While I have a privileged life, an amazing son, a partner that I love and who loves me, and a family that would do anything for me, I need a personal victory over this malaise. I need to make having a victory over this become a habit.

I abhor this unease, this dejection, and this depression. I know it will have its victories over me, but I need to win this war. I hope this feeling, like the solstice, is short and that there are brighter days ahead. That I will again be basking in the sun, feeling all the fortunes that I have, that the fog lifts and may it never return.

Fighting the virus.
Many have been doing something positive.
Some have pitched in to do their share to help others.

"Masks" have become commonplace.
And in many areas – mandatory.

Eeek -- like a criminal?
That's how you might feel when wearing a mask all the time.
But masks are the front line armor that protects us
against that nasty Covid-19. We are not the criminals.

Masks

Making Face Masks

by Jane Bechtel, RN

I am 72 years old and a retired registered nurse. My friend Vikki Russell asked me to tell the story of how my good friend and neighbor Mia Reale and I came to sew over four hundred face masks (we stopped counting once we reached 400) for disbursement to medical personnel, oncology offices, friends and families during the Covid-19 global pandemic of 2020. We are two of thousands of people who did, and continue to, make face masks.

We learned early in the crisis that personal protective equipment (PPE) for both medical and first-line responders was nearly exhausted. They were having to resort to reusing N95 and surgical masks that were designed for single use only. That's when the call went out to individuals and groups to create reusable masks for general use.

Mia and I both felt helpless, as much of the country did, but sewing masks (four different types) was something we could do to help. For over a month (March 2020 through April 2020), the two of us sewed eight to ten hours a day, six to seven days a week. It helped us cope with the anxiety and sense of helplessness associated with the first global pandemic in our lifetimes. And, I like to think that we helped others.

The use of cloth face masks became politicized unfortunately, despite scientific data proving that this simple public health measure significantly slows transmission of this virus.

As of December 1, 2020 at 16:02 GMT, there were 63,789,014 corona virus cases globally, along with 1,477,933 deaths. (https://www.worldometers.info/coronavirus). The United States of America data at that same time showed 13,933,434 cases with 274,723 deaths. I state this to remind everyone that the severity of this pandemic all occurred within 11 months.

Now in the second wave of Covid-19, PPE is diminishing, healthcare workers are exhausted and limited throughout the country. Mia and I are likely to be sewing away again.

Masks

by a physician in Virginia

The Covid-19 pandemic has done what most crises have done. It has brought out the best and the worst in people. It has now been a year and we have done what humans are so good at doing. We have adapted (and we have gained some perspective). Things were very different a year ago when it all came to a head in mid-March 2020, and by April and May there was so much confusion, lack of information, misinformation, panic, hoarding, selfishness, and lack of direction from the top, that I began to lose faith in my fellow humans.

There has been an ongoing shortage of personal protection equipment (PPE), including masks, and this was felt most acutely at the start of the pandemic.

There is a web site called Nextdoor and they send me a daily e-mail about happenings in our community. Someone named Tina put out a notice at the end of April 2020 stating that she was making masks and would give one or two of them free to anyone who needed one.

I replied to her message with: "Hi, I would like one or two of your masks. I work at a hospital and they are giving us only procedure masks and only one per day. Then they are collecting them at the end of the day, supposedly sterilizing them, and are planning to make us use them again (kind of gross). I've been keeping mine, cleaning it myself, and re-using it. Not a great idea either, but still better than wearing one that someone else had on. Anyway, my face is kind of small and the masks they give us don't fit well and are itchy. I bought myself some material and some bias tape and some elastic and will eventually make my own. I just haven't had the time to sit down and do it yet. Thank you for doing what you are doing!! I live a good half hour away from you, so I probably won't be able to get there until Friday after work or over the weekend. Please save me one or two. Thank you so very, very much!!"

On April 29, 2020, I received this message on *Nextdoor*: "Absolutely. I would be happy to save you a couple of masks. I make them a standard size but if you're handy with a needle and thread, you could always tighten the straps to fit you better if you need to... or just wash and dry... my first one shrunk a little after I washed it and dried it. Message me a day before you're able to come and I'll send my address... or if you want, I could slip it in the mail to you... whichever is easier for you."

I replied: "Wow. If you could mail me a couple of them, that would be wonderful. It would save me an hour of driving time. I will gladly send you a check for postage or we can use a more modern way of exchanging money (my kids do *venmo* and *zelle* and things like that." Then I included my cell phone number.

On 5/1/20, I received this text: "Hi, this is Tina. I have your masks ready to ship."

I replied: "Awesome. (I gave her my address). Please send me your address as well. I really want to make a tiny "donation" to cover postage and you can put the rest toward supplies to make more masks. The world needs more people like you. Stay safe and may only good things come your way!"

On 5/1/20, I received the following message on *Nextdoor* (late at night): "Hi, my daughter and I took a little road trip and delivered your masks to your mini-mailbox... I tucked them in there for ya! Blessings and be safe as well."

On 5/2/20, I received this text: "Good morning. I wanted to let you know my daughter and I delivered your masks to your small mailbox last night. I didn't want you to have to wait until Monday to get them. You too, be safe."

I replied: "I am speechless. Was working on the computer last night and saw that I had a message (on *Nextdoor*). When I saw that it was from you, I was expecting it to say that you were putting them in the mail and that it would have your address..."

Instead... I took a flashlight and went out and found your little brown package. That is the box that the newspaper gets put into and I didn't want the delivery man to accidentally take it thinking that I left it there for him. I brought them inside and tried them on right away. I was so excited and humbled by your kindness that I couldn't even get the words out properly as I told my daughter (who was still awake finishing a final for college) about the whole thing."

"Thank you doesn't say enough, not just for the two masks, but for the goodness inside of you that led to your making them in the first place and giving them away, but also the incredible generosity and selflessness that you would drive an hour to drop them off at my house and not accept anything in return."

"I will wash them this weekend and begin to wear them on Monday. I am a physician and am constantly coming in contact with people, some of whom are infected with Covid-19. There just isn't enough PPE for everyone."

"I am going to tell this story!
Keep warming the hearts of people.
Sometimes little things can make a profound difference."

On 5/2/20, I received this text: "Thank you so much for that kind response. Makes me teary eyed. The response from some of the people getting my masks has brought my heart so much joy, for me it makes the whole idea such a circle of blessings."

I saved our messages and our texts and forgot about them until recently when I was going through and deleting old ones. Again, I made the decision to save our correspondence. I have told people about my encounter with Tina, a person I have never met and yet would like to hug. This book is an opportunity to reach a wider audience and to tell the story of Tina and the masks to a lot of people all at once. I want to let readers know that there still are beautiful people in this world who are good to the core, and they are the ones that make life so worthwhile.

The Masks We Wear
by Aiden E. Nychka

So this is where we get them, the masks we wear.
Each day selectively picked, each day selectively paired.
For that crowd looks so innocent, clothed in red.
And yet controls our perfect face, personal expression dead.

We had a choice, once long ago
Before we cared, but better the devil they know,
Than the one that's truly you
the one lost in darkness, the one subdued

But have faith, my friend,
Your angel inside wants to ascend
For if a man like I, can shatter his porcelain face:
As can you, and let them notice

Unmasked

by Joan Shapiro

How strange to wear a mask in public
as if we waltzed at a Renaissance ball.
Or perhaps not so odd, in the Age of the Virus.
Instead, consider how selfish nowadays to be unmasked in a public place,
or to be bound up in a perversion, of anything resembling rational thought;
or to justify endangering others, without a modicum of introspection,
as if stupidity could be made sane by some peculiar notion of freedom.
The inalienable right to murder-by-contagion hasn't yet been enshrined
in the Constitution.

When many people drink the Kool-Aid
and join a violent political cult,
I suspect those people may not be able to engage in constructive colloquy.
When someone carries a tiki torch, or a firearm, or Confederate flag,
and angrily participates in a chanting mob
and snarls that he thinks that I (being Jewish)

am secretly plotting to rule the world,
it is very unlikely that he and I will join in verses of *Kumbaya*.

Long ago when I was misguided,
I thought it my mission to fix the world
and have enlightening discussions with bigots;
I thought I could change their point of view.
As I've gotten older I have learned the world can fix itself
— or not,
because it is not *my* job to fix *you.*
It is above my pay-grade, it is beyond my job description,
and it is because I am not Superwoman. Not even close.

When I see you in the grocery parking lot,
note your crass disregard for those who are sick,
and I'm treated to your insolent mask-less face;
when I witness your obvious scorn for survivors
altered by terrible after-effects; when I think
of the doctors, nurses, employees, all of whom suffer
from PTSD;
and all of those whose features will be forever and always
obscured by death —
and I watch you as you disrespect the heartache of loved
ones who have been left …

To me, giving up on *you* is my right.
You must fix yourself if you'd ever be free.

You have been enslaved by a hideous master
whose words advocate scorched earth and disaster.
When we face off in the parking lot
and I look in your lifeless eyes as you pass
and note your sneer from behind my mask,
I say *sotto voce,* “What an ass.”

conscious breathing

by Erin Robertson

Every time you breathe, you exhale some 25 sextillion (that's 2.5×10^{22}) molecules of oxygen – so many that with a day's breathing you will in all likelihood inhale at least one molecule from the breaths of every person who has ever lived. And every person who lives from now until the sun burns out will from time to time breathe in a bit of you. At the atomic level, we are in a sense eternal.

From *"The Body: A Guide for Occupants"* by Bill Bryson

breathing in the breath
of every being
that has been
fueled the same way
as despots and saints

breathing out the breath
that will become
part of every being to be
we are not so separate
not so alone
there's no way to fully distance
you from me

I take in courage and compassion
send out forgiveness and love
in case you need it

you -
my sons
Rosa the flycatcher patient on her nest
the bright orange wallflower feeding the fritillary
the garter snake sleeping sound under the tree roots
the man who tossed his cigarette butt on the trail today
the unmasked righteous person somewhere in my path
breathing out sentences nobody sees

We have all had to turn to our own "coping" mechanisms over the past year, here you may find a few new strategies.

For some it is nature, others creativity and one may find comfort in a daily routine. But we all appreciate assistance in coping when we can get it.

Coping

Still Swimming
by Rosemerry Wahtola Trommer

And so I pull the purple comb
through my son's thick hair,
the same way I've seen
the stylists do at Great Clips.
Wet the hair. Comb it through.
Part it. Hold it between
two fingers. Cut vertically. *Snip,*
and his hair falls to the floor.
Comb it through. *Snip. Snip.*

We both know that I
have no clue what I'm doing.
So we laugh as the hair
piles up on the floor.
We chatter, the way
a stylist and customer would,
talking of school and his friends
and his unruly cowlicks. *Snip.*

I remember that time
I was trapped underwater
by the river's hydraulics,
how I stared up at the light

shining through the surface
and thought, I don't think
it's my time yet to die.
And the river spit me out
and I swam hard as I could
through the rapid toward shore.

I don't think it's my time yet
to die. Nor my son's. Though
all around us the news of dying —
the numbers increasing every day,
stories of beloveds who are gone.

We ask ourselves, how do we
go on? And meanwhile, we do.
We go on. And because my son's hair
is too long for his taste,
I learn how to cut it by cutting it.
How much more will we learn
as this goes on? How to share?
How to grieve? How to let go? How to live?

And meanwhile, life spits us out
into sunlight, and we come up into another day
spluttering, gasping, surprised
we're alive, and we swim, what a gift
to find we're still swimming.

What I Saw on a Walk in Early Evening on the First Day of Spring in the First Pandemic Year

by Lynda La Rocca

Daffodils and violets,
dog rolling on her back, paws pedaling
to sky,
sun sinking through stained glass,
spilling ruby rays to greening ground,
eight turkey vultures roosting in
the branches of a pine tree,
mule deer buck with one antler,
girl on a skateboard, waving hello,
gold light
behind lace curtain,
one candle in the window,
gleaming past the grief,
the gloom.

Covid changed our lives

by Alexandra Hudson; Edited by Mike Collett-White

On Jan. 1, 2020, as the world welcomed a new decade, Chinese authorities in Wuhan shut down a seafood market in the central city of 11-million, suspecting that an outbreak of a new "viral pneumonia" affecting 27-people might be linked to the site.

Early lab tests in China pointed to a new coronavirus. By Jan. 20 it had spread to three countries.

For most people, it was a minor health scare unfolding half a world away.

Nearly a year later it has changed lives fundamentally. Almost everyone has been affected, be it through illness, losing loved ones or jobs, being confined at home and having to get used to a whole new way of working, relaxing and interacting.

As of December 1, 2020 almost 1.5-million people had died globally from the Covid-19 disease related to the coronavirus, and some 63-million people had been infected.

After the initial "wave" of the pandemic was brought under some semblance of control in many countries, nations are now fighting second and third waves even greater than the first, forcing new restrictions on everyday life.

Among the most haunting images to emerge from the pandemic in 2020 are those of medics on the frontlines of the battle against the virus.

In Milan's San Raffaele hospital, seven intensive care unit staff attended to an 18 year-old patient suffering from Covid-19, pushing the bed into the ward and holding medical equipment and monitors.

Doctors and nurses like them swathed in protective gear — gowns, gloves, masks, and visors, some with their names or initials written on their uniforms — have become a familiar sight.

So, too, have images of medics collapsing from exhaustion or grief at losing one of their own to the disease.

By March and April many countries began to impose lockdowns and social distancing to slow the spread of the highly contagious virus.

Structures to separate and protect people sprang up - from transparent screens at supermarket checkouts to the plastic sheet which allowed 83 year-old Lily Hendrickx, a resident at a Belgian nursing home, to hug Marie-Christine Desoer, the home's director.

The effects on the natural world of the shutdown were sometimes astonishing. Birdsong could be heard like never before in towns and wild animals ventured into newly empty cities.

At the usually crowded Golden Gate Bridge View Vista Point across from San Francisco, a coyote stood by the roadside. Even the streets of Manhattan were eerily empty.

Ballet dancer Ashlee Montague donned a gas mask and danced in the middle of Times Square, New York.

In Brazil's capital, Brasilia, Catholic priest Jonathan Costa prayed alone at the Santuario Dom Bosco church, among photographs of the faithful, attached to the pews.

Wearing masks to combat the spread of the virus became commonplace the world over.

At Tokyo's Shinagawa train station, crowds of commuters wore face masks, as did prisoners crowded into a cell in El Salvador's Quezaltepeque jail.

In private homes, families learned to live together 24 hours a day and how to entertain and teach their children.

In San Fiorano in northern Italy, school teacher Marzio Toniolo, 35, took a picture of his two year-old daughter Bianca painting his toenails bright red.

The pandemic hit some of the world's poorest people the hardest — exposing the inequalities in access to medical treatment and in government funds to compensate people who lost their livelihoods.

In South Africa in May, at the Itireleng informal settlement near Laudium suburb in Pretoria, people waited in a queue that stretched as far as the eye could see to receive food aid.

As 2020 headed to its close, vaccines were on the horizon. There is hope that some aspects of life as we knew it will return.

A Skirt for 2020

by Kara Bussell

Covid-19 seems to be a challenge for everyone in different ways. People pick their coping mechanisms to help them through and drawing was one of mine.

2020, although extremely challenging, also held a lot of personal growth for me (and I'm sure many others). I definitely explored more of my spiritual and creative side.

My son was two years-old at the time and we had a whole lot more time at home together, that was both challenging and amazing at the same time. (Our hand prints are on the skirt). My son's father was stuck on the other side of the border so he unfortunately missed a lot of time with us.

Art relaxes me and makes me feel calm... I used a second hand bed sheet and turned it into a skirt to then draw on for the entire year of 2020. I used it as a means of meditation and some of the patterns on the skirt have meaning to me.

The Moon... I had so many dreams about the moon in 2020. I looked at the moon all the time and it made me feel amazing, free and calm

Dragonflies... They were everywhere, everyday, while I was in lockdown. Maybe I just took more notice of what was around me in nature

Crickets... I saw a whole lot of crickets.. I took this as a sign of good luck ;)

Sacred/angel numbers... 1111 and 2222 showed up so many times. I'd never noticed them before this point and decided to take them as signs. This is when I started learning about spirituality and sacred numbers

Zentangle... I used these patterns to feel completely calm and relaxed

During this time I also learned to listen to myself and do things in alignment with how I'm feeling, which has made so much difference in my life.

I feel 2020 had so much personal growth for me and although it was in hard times, it also shows what people are really capable of. I've seen some absolutely amazing stories of people helping each other and beautiful creations that have come out of these difficult times.

A Skirt for 2020

by Kara Bussell

Quiche recipe

by Lorrie Herranz

This is a flexible and versatile recipe to use up all those left-overs, or soon-to-expire ingredients, in your fridge. Be creative; adjust the recipe to use what you have on hand. This is a great recipe template to postpone that shopping trip to the supermarket and a go-to recipe for any stay-at-home time period.

Use any size pie pan, quiche dish, lasagna dish, brownie dish, or similar.

I make this without crust because it's easier. If you want crust, make your favorite buttery crust recipe or buy a pre-made one.

For the custard, mix eggs and milk. For a regular size pie pan use four eggs and one to one-1/2 cups milk. I use 10 to 12 eggs for an 11-inch diameter x two inches tall straight-sided round dish. Adjust accordingly to your pan or dish. Season with herbs that go with your filling.

For the filling, chop up a variety of cheeses, vegetables, and meat if you want. Leftovers are perfect for this.

Butter the pan. Set oven for 425.

PRO TIP: If you are using a crust, add the cheese on top of crust to prevent the crust from getting soggy. Then add the filling, and then pour the custard on top.

If you are not using a crust, mix the filling ingredients with the custard and pour into the dish.

Bake at 425 degrees for 35 to 45 minutes, depending on the size. The quiche will puff up and then go down. The quiche is done when browned on the top and a toothpick or knife poked in the center comes out clean.

When Contemplating April
by Paula Gordon Lepp

The day I finally HAD ENOUGH of being
the “Keeper Of Everyone’s Schedule”
I went and bought a calendar.

You know the kind... one month at a glance,
big white squares, pithy little quotes.
And for the next two years
at the end of each month,
I filled in next month’s blank spaces with
everything for all of us. Everything.
Classes, lessons, activities, rehearsals, appointments,
doctor’s visits, meetings, events, work schedules,
gigs, holidays, birthdays, anniversaries, trips, and
marked chunks of time when my husband traveled
when my son would be home from college,
when my daughter had tech week and show dates.
An accounting of days for considerate eyes.

I look at this March just past
still hanging on the door
divided almost perfectly between Before
and After.
Two weeks of days full, some almost bursting
with all the things

followed by two weeks of days being swallowed
one after another by red X after red X,
the question of "What are we doing today?"
no longer being voiced.

And so today I hang April,
even though there is no
everything.
April, with its month of clean, white squares.
A field, a prairie of unencumbered days,
no tethers
no bounds,
willing me to fill each day
not with obligation,
but intention.
With gratefulness,
not despair.

In a time of confusion
sometimes all you need is to clear your mind.

One way – a very long distance run.
Another – get reacquainted with nature.
But we promise you, get your body moving and it will help,
both physically and mentally.

Exercise

Two Weeks Living and Running with Coronavirus
by Sarah Lavender Smith

Originally published in April 2020 on Trail Runner Magazine's *website*

March 15, the second Sunday of the month, I wake early in a hotel room in Boulder to run in Chautauqua Park. Pink light illuminates the massive rock formations of the Flatirons, but I barely notice the view. I am so wound up with worry that I see only mental images that flip like flashcards, each involving a family member, every thought layered with news of the pandemic.

I picture my son's dorm room that we need to pack up this morning so we can move him back home. At least he's with us now, but my daughter needs to get back from Rhode Island. She is struggling to vacate her apartment and catch a flight. Her senior year in college is ending abruptly — how can this be? She's prone to recurrent infections that need medicine. What if she catches this virus?

Client work for my husband's business abruptly dried up. He has enough in the bank to make today's payroll, but how will he pay the staff in the coming weeks? It scares me to see his face so grim as he toggles his screen between QuickBooks and CNN. The market surely will tank when it opens tomorrow. The ski resort closed yesterday. So many friends out of work.

As I run, I feel yesterday's embrace of Mom. We stopped to see her on the way to Boulder, and I had to talk my way in, because it was the first day they tried to enforce visitor restrictions. I stroked her shoulders as she sat on her bed in the memory-care unit of the assisted-living home. I inhaled her smell and studied her body in case I never get that close again. Her caregivers eyed me suspiciously, as if I might bring in germs no matter how much I scrub my hands and cover my face. "I just hope we stay healthy to take care of them," one said in a low voice to me.

The fact that my races are getting canceled barely registers, except I feel some relief. March through May, I was supposed to travel to Moab, then Sonoma, then Boston, then Hawaii for ultras and the marathon. Now training is one less thing to worry about. I need to run for health, not sport.

On a flat stretch, I do a set of strides while repeating the mantra, *I am healthy, I am strong*. I read somewhere that to cope with anxiety, it helps to repeat positive affirmations, so I say those phrases and try not to think, *I can't get sick, we can't afford this.*

If so much can change in a mere two weeks — from when our routines were normal and the economy hummed along, to social distancing and shuttered restaurants — then how unrecognizable would the world be in 14 more days? Our little corner of Colorado will be OK, right?

I can't imagine as I run that exactly two weeks from now, my 53-year-old husband Morgan—my best friend since high school, my everything—would be lying in a hospital room, the eighth person in our county to test positive for Covid-19.

Morgan would see his oxygen saturation level dip dangerously as viral pneumonia attacks his lungs, and he'd wonder if he was about to enter critical care for a ventilator. He would ask himself, "Is this where it ends?"

And I would be at home with my kids, weeping when I catch sight of his jacket and hat on the coat rack. I would wonder if he'll live to come back and wear them again.

***

On the drive home from Boulder, our son Kyle keeps asking to turn on the air conditioner. "It's so hot in here," he says, except it isn't. I'm wearing winter clothes, and the temperature feels fine to me.

The next day, Kyle mostly stays in bed sleeping, coughing and developing congestion. Part of me worries it could be the virus. A few people have tested positive in Boulder, including a worker in their cafeteria. But I tend to believe him when he says, "It's just a cold. I'm fine."

I drive to the airport to fetch our daughter Colly, who is exhausted from packing and traveling. A day later, her long-term boyfriend moves in with us from California for an indefinite period. Welcoming him feels like the right thing to do, because he makes our daughter happier and he's almost like family. But we keep his presence secret, because soon after he arrives, the county decrees that all visitors have to return home.

We collectively commit to quarantine. I go from empty-nester to cook-and-housecleaner-in-chief for three young adults, relishing the sense of purpose and distraction from the news.

Kyle feels good again after a few days, and this unexpectedly pleasant week feels like a stay-cation. The boys play chess while my daughter makes funny TikTok videos. I run on remote dirt roads. Morgan channels the stress from his business into building a chicken coop, and we all play with the baby chickens that we keep in a box inside the house.

Then, about five days after the trip to Boulder, Morgan starts coughing. That weekend, Colly and I develop a dry cough, too. Thank goodness, her boyfriend never shows any sign of illness.

I meet someone to run on the third Sunday of the month. We park far apart from each other, and I shout through the car window, "I might be getting sick, and my son's been sick, so keep your distance!"

We run a double-wide path through mud and slushy snow, always at least six feet apart, but it doesn't feel right, as much as I enjoy her company. I decide to run alone from now on, because what if I'm contagious? Plus, I don't want to feel pressure to keep up with anyone. I'm so tired, I mostly want to hike.

I feel a little hot and light-headed when I return home, so I take my temperature. In the high altitude where we live, 97.6 is normal. I'm a little over 99. A sense of dread returns to my stomach.

Colly wanders downstairs looking extra pale and sweaty. "Not great," she answers when asked how she's feeling. Her temperature is around 99. I wipe the thermometer with alcohol and get Morgan to take his temperature. He has a low fever too.

"Well, this could be the best thing ever!" he says, and it's hard to tell if he's serious or joking. "We'll all have a mild case and then be immune." We don't bother going to the local medical center, because hardly any coronavirus tests are available, and they're reserved for serious cases.

I allow myself a rest day and run five miles the next, hiking every uphill because my muscles feel extra weak. But I can breathe deeply, and I'm confident my lungs are strong.

I don't get sick, I tell myself. *Movement is medicine.*

By Wednesday afternoon, my daughter and I feel close to normal again, but Morgan is worsening. I find him outside on a stepladder, trying to hammer the roof on the almost-finished chicken coop before the next storm hits. His eyes look sunken and his skin is flushed. He admits he needs a nap.

He's been taking three-hour naps recently. Not only is he profoundly tired and mildly feverish, but he also has severe muscle aches around his trunk. His skin feels sensitive to the touch. He says he feels like he has a combination of mononucleosis and shingles.

He gets in daily contact with the Telluride Medical Center, a small facility with only a handful of doctors and nurses. The doctor over the phone concludes Morgan is not in respiratory distress. He can breathe well and hold his breath for 10+ seconds without coughing. Self-care at home is the best and only option.

For the next three days, Morgan stays in bed while drifting in and out of sleep. During this time, I email a running friend, "I've been up since 2:30 a.m. with anxiety—I literally have wondered if he's starting the process of dying because he can't get out of bed and feels so bad, but then I remind myself he's breathing fine and his temp is only about a degree above normal."

On Saturday at bedtime, I lay down next to Morgan. I refuse to leave his side to distance myself from his germs because I want to count his breaths per minute and monitor his cough.

Almost every one of his exhalations has become a mini-cough. His breathing is rapid, 38 to 40 breaths a minute, double or triple normal. When I turn on the bedside light, his skin looks grayish.

"Talk to me," I say.

"OK. Need shower." Driven by a desire to reduce the aches and cool off, he stumbles into the bathroom and manages a quick shower. I help him back to bed and take his temperature.

His fever has spiked to 103. "We need to go to the hospital now," I say calmly.

"Tomorrow," he mumbles. But I know we can't wait. I call the after-hours doctor at the med center and tell him my husband needs a chest scan and is having trouble breathing. He and a nurse prepare for our arrival.

Somehow, around 1-am, I get Morgan into the car — he moves in slow motion, he looks as if he has aged 20 years — and I drive the six miles to town, at one point swerving to avoid an elk. Morgan doesn't notice the elk herd lining the road because he's barely conscious.

Town is dark and feels deserted. The lone doctor and nurse meet us in the ER's doorway wearing haz-mat suits. We put a mask on Morgan and guide him inside by his elbows.

The nurse immediately puts an oxygen-saturation monitor on his finger and sees a reading of 74 percent, indicating severe hypoxia. She puts a cannula in his nostrils so supplemental oxygen can flow to his system. Within minutes, his level rises above 90, out of the danger zone, and the nurse looks relieved. Morgan opens his eyes and says, "Oh my God, that feels so much better."

The nurse gives him a regular flu test, which is negative, then administers the Covid swab test. It will take five days to get the result back confirming he's positive.

The doctor calls a radiologist to come in around 2-am for a chest CT scan. They waste no time sharing the news: "We see bilateral viral pneumonia with the patchy pattern characteristic of Covid."

Morgan looks brave, so I try to look brave too. But we both know there's no treatment, only management, of this horribly stealthy virus. He had bacterial pneumonia five years ago, with wheezy fluid-filled lungs and chest pressure, but this type of pneumonia did not present any of those telltale signs.

Morgan will need round-the-clock care and potentially a ventilator, so I prepare to drive him an hour and twenty minutes to the nearest hospital in Montrose. We stop by our house on the way to pack some things and tell the kids.

I enter their bedrooms around 3:30-am and say, "Get dressed and come down, your dad needs to talk." They instantly sense the seriousness and hurry down.

Sitting on the bench in our entranceway, a portable oxygen tank attached to his nose with thin tubes, Morgan rallies to explain his diagnosis to the kids in a reassuring voice. "The good news is," he says — because he always tries to stay positive — "the hospital is not crowded, and if I need a ventilator, they've got one."

Colly and Kyle stand blinking in the light, telling him he'll be OK and promising to take care of the animals. They take turns hugging him and saying they love him.

I know this may be the last time they see their father for days — forever? — so there is no way I'm going to tell them to refrain from hugging because of his contagion, but I do remind them to wash their hands.

I pack a small bag for myself, intending to stay at the hospital. Only when we arrive at the parking lot does it hit me that I have to drop Morgan off and leave. A security guard is apologizing, but insisting that I can't enter if I might be contagious.

I get in the back seat where Morgan sits with the oxygen tank. I'm all business — "you got your phone, your charger? I put a book in your bag that I think you'll like" — and then I feel my face crumple and can't even say goodbye. I hold his shoulders to pull him closer, and he hugs me back.

"Call me, text me, promise," I say.

“I will.” He gets out with the help of a nurse in protective gear.

I pull myself together to drive home. The route skirts the snow-covered 14’er Sneffels, and as I look at that craggy peak glowing at sunrise, I imagine how my grandpa’s brother, Dwight Lavender, must have looked when he did so much mountaineering on those slopes as a young man in the early 1930s. He was a famous climber until he caught the polio virus and died in less than 72 hours at age 23. If it happened to him, it can happen to Morgan. No matter how strong we are, we are vulnerable without vaccines and other medicine.

My mind spins into scenarios of life without my husband. I want to celebrate our 30th anniversary this June, I want him at our kids’ weddings if they get married.

Being an ultrarunner doesn’t exactly prepare me for a moment like this, except that the phrase I repeated during the most fatiguing moments my last self-supported stage race comes back to me: *Get through it.* Quitting is not an option.

When I get home, I’m relieved Morgan answers my call and can talk. He says the doctor put him on two types of antibiotics and told him, “We’ll know soon enough if these are any help.” Either he’ll stabilize, or he’ll enter critical care. (Antibiotics don't fight the virus itself, but many doctors prescribe them for the coronavirus to fight any secondary infection and to try to reduce lung inflammation.)

I try to catch up on sleep, but I can't. So I get dressed and go for a run, but I can't. My legs feel like they might give out. I hike to the half-mile point up the road and turn back, walking slowly and using this time to cry out of sight of others.

I have trouble sleeping that night and long for the sound of Morgan's breathing. When I call the hospital in the morning, a nurse informs me she had to increase his oxygen to get his saturation level back up. I interpret the chilling news as a sign his lungs are giving out.

When I get through to talk to Morgan, he says, "I thought that was it, that I'm going down" when he couldn't get enough oxygen, "so I really tried to think through what was going on." He realized his nose felt extra stuffy, so he asked a nurse to flush out his nostrils with saline drops, and then he could breathe better.

"I'm hoping my problem is just boogers," he says, and we both laugh a little.

"You know," I say, "if you have to go to the ICU, then you'll need to decide whether you want to stay there. Because you'll be alone at the end and sedated, but I could come get you and bring you home." My voice breaks. "I think it would be better to have you here with us if you're not getting better, so you need to talk to your doctor about this while you can."

"I know," he says, "I thought of that."

***

Morgan doesn't need intensive care. After about 36 hours, I get a call telling me he can recover at home.

I'm slightly disbelieving. It feels like we won a coin toss: Morgan gets to come home; others stay in the hospital and die alone. But I'm flooded with relief as I speed through the long drive back to get him.

He'll need to be hooked up to oxygen for many days, maybe weeks. He'll get drenched with night sweats and suffer more headaches. His diminished sense of smell and taste will be slow to return. Time will tell if he'll get well enough to enjoy high-altitude hikes this summer. But we are together, and each day he seems a little more like himself.

I wait five days to try running again, and when I do, I'm nervous. Running might make me feel sick and weak. I've lost faith in repeating, "I am healthy, I am strong." I still fear the virus in us.

I commit to go slowly and limit myself to three miles. My legs feel better from all the rest. I notice how much the snow has melted in just a week, because we're into April. A virus can't stop the seasons.

I suddenly need to hear the passage from Ecclesiastes, for the reminder that humans always get through dark times, so I play The Byrds' *Turn, Turn* on my phone as I run.

A time to kill, a time to heal. A time to laugh, a time to weep.

I have to walk for a bit as the music continues so that I can process one last cleansing cry, and as I do, I mentally add these phrases to the song: *A time to rest, a time to run.*

One moment

by Paula Gordon Lepp

Today, my heart
is a fist clenched tight,
letting nothing out,
nothing in.

So I go to the woods..
where the sun embraces me
with her warmth,
the wind whispers psalms
in my ear,
the trees sway with joy,
inviting me to dance,
and the rocks
stand watch, ever faithful,
steadfast.

It's their offering
for me to accept.
Or not.
And just for a moment,
my heart loosens...
just for a moment.

Some days, oh
some days,
that moment is
everything.

Lost and Found

by Sam Morton

I was living my best life in Washington, D.C. when Covid-19 hit in late March of 2020. I was fresh out of undergraduate, working for a premier environmental research institute, getting ready to move to Amsterdam for my Masters, preparing for my first marathon, and finally — *finally* hitting the dating scene. Then it all came to a grinding halt.

I decided to defer graduate school. The marathon was canceled. My friends scattered, including myself, and all I had left to cling to was a remote job from the suburbs of my parents' home.

Like everyone, Covid-19 shattered my life. My friends' loved ones got sick, and then died, and my sister — an artist living in New York City — holed herself up in her apartment and only called to yell at me through the phone until I refused to speak to her at all. I felt like I was disappearing, losing all sense of time, reality, and identity. My eating disorder began to creep out of whatever den I shoved it into after college. I went through long periods of sluggish despair, and then short bursts of wild energy.

By late May I knew I needed a change — desperately. I could not continue to work out of my parent's home, pounding the same dull cement sidewalks day after day until the pandemic came to an unforeseeable end. I started making day trips to the start of Appalachian Trail in Fannin County, Georgia. I did not know anything about trail running, but I did know nature and running were my best chance of fighting off an encroaching bout of mental illness. Wearing my old minimalist road shoes and lacking any way to carry food or water, I ran through those Appalachia woods for ten, sometimes twenty, miles. Amidst the silence I found the answers to my problems.

Two months later I am running up a steep grade in the Colorado Rockies with my pink fastpack stuffed to the brim, a dusty pair of Solomon's on my feet, and a delirious smile plastered to my face. I am about to summit Imogene Pass for the second time in twenty-four hours, after running from Telluride to Ouray the day before, feasting on cold lentils, and camping alone on the side of a dirt road.

I smell of sweat and evergreen, and my skin prickles with frigid mid-summer alpine air, keeping me restless most the night. I am awoken at dawn by a curious coyote. She sniffs at my face for a few short-breathed moments, then loses interest and darts back into the woods. I wiggle out of my bivy sack, pull on a pair of dew-damp shorts, and pick my way up Tomboy Road. The extra elevation gain back to Telluride is brutal, but entirely worth it when I make the final ascent. I breath in sharp atmosphere, tinged with the sweet smell of

Sam Morton's view from the top of Imogene Pass

ATV exhaust fumes which zoom past wordlessly with their Hayduke beer chests jostling on the rack.

I sit down on a rock away from the crowd of tourists and enjoy a brownie I have saved for this very occasion. I am not thinking about work, or the pandemic, or my eating disorder. I am, perhaps for the first time, living in the moment, awash with amazement of what the body is capable of when fueled correctly — spiritually and physically.

That is the gift trail running has given to me. Running is my Covid-19 savior, and for that I am truly grateful. Without it, anorexia coupled with depression may have eaten away at me bit by bit like so many others this year. Although I move to Europe for graduate school in the fall, I will leave a part of me on these Colorado trails. They have given me hope, strength, confidence, and humility all at once. I know other runners have found this. My hope is that the rest of the world might find it too.

This virus has affected all of our lives.
We have all now experienced "loss" due to this health crisis;
the deaths of family members, friends and neighbors.

End of life happens. Sometimes all too suddenly.
But death marks not only the end of a life, but enables the commemoration of that life.

Loss

No Touch of a Hand

by Laura Kudo

My father passed away on August 16, 2020 suddenly and very quickly from Covid-19. He was a strong, healthy 79 year-old man who would greet family and friends alike with a bear hug that could almost squeeze the breath out of you. He had no pre-existing conditions and had never spent a single night in a hospital in his entire life. He was gone in four weeks. Every horrid, awful, tragic news story you have seen of how people with Covid-19 die hooked up to a ventilator, cordoned off through heavy glass, no words or touches, comfort or personal contact from the family, alone, isolated... this is my family's story.

Unfortunately, we also did not have the "in touch" terrific hospital staff that sings Amazing Grace and embraces the family and loved ones... my Father passed in a sterile, antiseptic, sad and dark environment in the middle of a humid, mid-west night, while we watched from the corridor of a cold hospital wing. There was my sweet, precious Mother sitting on an unwelcome, hard folding chair, her prayer book clutched in her tiny hand, with the surreal reality of my Father's last breath and heartbeat unfolding before her like a horrible nightmare where you wake up gasping for breath. Except it was real. And she couldn't even touch his hand.

Beyond the trauma of the way my Father passed, our family has continued to be reminded daily of *how* he passed. There is not a day that has gone by since his passing that Covid-19 has not dominated the news on every level, every day; has even dominated most social conversation, and has impacted almost every aspect of our daily lives. We cannot gather with family (we had to spend Thanksgiving, Christmas and my Mother's birthday apart), spend time with close friends... cannot even get the simplest of comforts like a hug from a neighbor. Cannot grieve, laugh, cry, and share stories with friends and loved ones in person. How does one heal in this environment?

I and my family are comforted by our faith, and the healing *will* begin at some point. Until then, our hearts are with those families that know our grief and sorrow first hand.

Gone But Not Forgotten

by Dr. Margaret Bernice Smith Bristow

The phone rang early at 7 am March 30, 2020. 46 years ago was the last time my phone rang so early. That time it was a call from the nurse telling me my father had passed. So, I had a little melancholy taking up real estate space in my head. But I thought, "I know damn well those telemarketers are not calling me this damn early!"

"Hello," I answered. Happy, happy to see it was Mary. She had been our trip coordinator when we went on several vacations outside the U.S., Brazil and Argentina, and most recently South Africa in 2017. We were all looking forward to her planning our next and newest trip: Australia, New Zealand and the Fiji Islands for November four through the 24th, 2020. But news of Covid had hit.

A year ago I had put my down payment on my seat through GoAheadTours. "Mary, Mary, girl I thought the doctors would not have allowed you to call anyone." (She worked as an emergency RN in New York and came home on Wednesdays to Willingboro, NJ where she had a home right across the street from my sister. Mary had caught Covid-19 and had been on a ventilator.)

"Bernice, it is ok. I am not going to be on the phone long." I want you to know we will go to Australia," she said in a slow, but strong voice.

I eagerly replied, "And we will go to New Zealand. Ain't that right, Mary?"

"Yes," she answered with enthusiasm in her voice.

"And we're gonna go to the Fiji Islands, too," I chimed.

"Yes, you know we will!"

Well, we talked further and Mary continued, "Bernice, I thought I would hit the jackpot before I caught this thing!"

"But Mary, praise the Lord. You beat it. You sound good, girl."

"Bernice, I can't talk too long," she said.

"Well, can I call you back this evening?" I asked.

"Yes." And we hung up.

I called my sisters, telling them how well she sounded. Telling them that she reassured me we would all go on that vacation we had been planning on for over a year.

Hours later that same afternoon, I was riding in the car with my youngest sister, having told her about Mary's recovery. "What! she blurted. Mary. Oh, not Mary!"

"What?" I interjected. "What happened to Mary?"

"She's dead," my sister replied.

"Dead, I just talked to her this morning."

And so ends my first encounter with one victim of this pernicious virus that continues to claim so many lives.

In The Caribbean

by Coleen Moore

2020 began with a Caribbean cruise in January. For the entire month of February I was quarantined in my bedroom with Covid 19. I lived with my 98-year-old Father and didn't want him to catch "whatever" I had. In March, April and May he fought me every step of the way, NOT to be quarantined.

On May 29, he fell during the night and hit his head. We weren't allowed to see him in the hospital due to Covid. After two days, a wonderful nurse from hospice got us into the facility the hospital had transferred him to. He was dying. She had him transferred to hospice. We were able to be with him there. He died after four days.

In June, we had a graveside memorial service. In July, my daughter convinced me to move to Virginia Beach. I put my house on the market. In August, my house sold and I bought a condo. Sight unseen due to Covid. On Sept 4, I moved into the condo. It needed a lot of work. I would have offered less, but sight unseen, the realtor took advantage of me.

In October, I turned 66 years old. I sat on the beach behind my condo with tears running down my face. I had enormous guilt, grief, fear, anger and joy. All of the trauma of losing my father, being financially taken advantage of, joy at living close to my daughter and grandsons, sadness at clearing out my parents' house of 47 years of memories. All while my life was endangered by the people who packed me, moved me, unloaded me, sold me, told me my Dad was dying, buried him, bought his car, delivered my new furniture and gave my cat a rabies shot so he could live in the condo.

In November my emotions stabilized. My old resilience returned. My nightmares lessened and I slept well. In December the news announced a vaccine is coming soon. I talked to my daughter and son-in-law about taking them to Disney World. I think I'm back to my old self. Bye 2020, I'll never forget you, unfortunately.

Won't Shop The Same Again

by Paula Gordon Lepp

She had her arm buried up to her
elbow in the marked-down items that filled
a shopping cart repurposed as clearance bin
parked beside the discounted bread,
bright yellow Yahoo! sale stickers almost glowing
under the fluorescent lights, canned goods hidden
under a cardboard mountain of granola bars
no doubt put there by an indifferent teen
with a haphazard regard for physics.

I offered to help. She looked at me
with her rheumy eyes, her spidery voice
muffled through the cloth mask, "No, it's ok.
You are no doubt busy. I'm just trying to get
to this small can of corn way down at the bottom."
I told her I didn't mind. Such a small gesture, really.
With a little eco-friendly mountaintop removal, I razed
away the granola, exposing the cans to her scrutiny.

"Look! They are only 19 cents! I think I'll
get two!" She straightened slightly, a small, curved
study in triumph, one niblet-filled trophy clutched
in each hand. She dropped them into her cart,
and thanked me for my help. I spotted another can,

picked it up and asked her if she wanted it as well.

She looked at me, a ghost of a smile. “Two is probably
one more than I need, but who can pass up that deal?”
Then, “I have been cooking for me and my family, and
once the kids were grown, for me and my husband for what
seems like forever. We were married 61 years last year.
My Benny died of Covid in November.
I am still trying to learn how to cook for one.”

She cocked her head to one side, piercing me
with her eyes, the patina of decades of
hard won wisdom burnishing her words.
“Never take for granted buying the big can”

She turned and shuffled her cart away,
and oh the weight of that one small can,
so incredibly heavy in my hand.

The Space Between
by Aiden E. Nychka

When someone dies they leave a hole,
And in that hole they are laid to rest.
Above their breast we leave a stone,
Then all alone we leave their bones.
Seeds are sewn and the stone grows old
The dates are forgotten but the dash, forever serene
It's the space between, that friends will read
And forever relive in childish memory.

Jacqueline Joan (Kavaney) Kapsner

Kapsner (Kavaney), Jacqueline Joan age 81, died on December 3rd in Minneapolis of Covid-19. Jackie was born on May 27th, 1939 in Bismarck, North Dakota to Esther and Jack Kavaney, the first of three daughters.

When Jackie was five years old, her father was killed in action in St. Lô, France, an infantryman in the battle for Europe. Two years later her mother, Esther, married Fred Rohs, also a veteran of the conflict, and the family moved to York, Nebraska. Jackie was proud of her roots in North Dakota and Nebraska, though she was bound and determined to leave small town life for the big city. When she graduated from St. Joseph High School in 1957 she moved to St. Paul, Minnesota and attended nursing school at the College of St. Catherine.

She met a slightly older medical student by the name of Adrian Kapsner while attending a party with one of Adrian's close friends. They were married at St. John's Abbey Church, the first to be wed in the Marcel Breuer-designed masterpiece, and moved to Hutchinson, Minnesota, where Adrian began his career in medicine.

At her first dinner party, she served a single roast duck to eight people, an early sign that cooking would not be high on her list of interests. They had three boys in quick succession:

Christopher, Jonathan and Matthew. When Adrian was drafted into the United States Army during the Vietnam War, the young family moved to Bethesda, Maryland, where Adrian was stationed at Fort Dietrich. Jackie would never forget the comforts of military life, often comparing their time at Fort Dietrich to a stay at a country club.

While in Maryland, Jackie gave birth to their only daughter, Kitty, named for Jackie's grandmother and sister. After Adrian's discharge they moved back to the upper Midwest and lived in Bloomington, Minnesota and Eau Claire, Wisconsin before landing in Edina, Minnesota in 1973.

Once her children were in school full time, Jackie went to work at Harold's clothing store in downtown Minneapolis and then the Side Door in Wayzata, Minnesota. Her closets were stuffed with the clothing she bought while working, her diminished pay checks reflecting her obsession, and her Black Irish beauty combined with her impeccable style made her the belle of the ball. Besides fashion, Jackie had a deep appreciation for art, and kept current with foreign films and literature. Over the years her bedroom took on the appearance of a used bookstore, with books stacked on every table and piled on the floor, even shoved under the bed.

She also loved music, listening to everything from George Jones to Elvis and Bob Dylan, even enjoying the Punk and New Wave music she would hear coming from her children's bedrooms. She and Adrian traveled the world, golfing Ireland and Scotland with friends and visiting their children wherever they lived, whether it was New York City, Spain, Turkey, India, or New Zealand. Jackie was very involved in her children's and grandchildren's lives, spending hours on the phone catching up almost daily, chatting about movies, politics, books and even football.

There will be a profound absence in all our lives knowing she'll never call again. Jackie was preceded in death by her parents, Jack, Esther and Fred; and her sister, Kitty. Three days after her death, she was joined by Adrian, her adoring husband of 59 years. She is survived by her four children, Christopher, Jonathan, Matthew and Kitty; eight grandchildren and one great grandchild. Also, her beloved sister Judy Hodell, and many nieces and nephews. Funeral arrangements to be announced when it's safe to gather again. In lieu of flowers donations can be made in the name of Adrian and Jackie Kapsner to the Minnesota Orchestra or St. John's University, Collegeville, MN.

Adrian Leroy Kapsner

Kapsner, Adrian Leroy age 85, died on December 6th in Minneapolis of Covid-19. Adrian was born on February 10th, 1935 in Starbuck, Minnesota to Alex and Aletha Kapsner, who owned the local pharmacy.

Adrian had an idyllic childhood in that small town along the shores of Lake Minnewaska. He would fondly reminisce about Starbuck for the rest of his life, but at the age of eleven the family moved to Princeton, Minnesota where Adrian would become a star athlete, playing basketball, baseball and football. He played center and linebacker on the Princeton High School football team and was named to the Minnesota All-Star team in 1953.

He attended St. John's University, like many Kapsner men before and after him. Much to the chagrin of newly-appointed, and now legendary, head coach John Gagliardi, Adrian dropped football in his freshman year to concentrate on his pre-med studies. He graduated from St. John's in 1957 and attended the University of Minnesota Medical School. In 1960 Adrian met the love of his life, Jacqueline Kavaney, at a medical school fraternity party. Jackie was at the party with one of his best friends, but that didn't discourage Adrian, and she agreed to a single date to have a Coke so he would leave her alone. They were married at St. John's Abbey Church, the first couple to be wed in the Marcel Breuer-designed modern masterpiece, and moved to Hutchinson, Minnesota where Adrian began his career in medicine.

Jackie soon gave birth to their oldest son, Christopher, who was quickly followed by Jonathan and Matthew. When Adrian was drafted into the United States Army during the Vietnam War the young family moved to Fort Dietrich, Maryland, where their daughter Kitty was born. Upon his discharge from the military, the family moved back to the upper Midwest, living in Bloomington, Minnesota and then Eau Claire, Wisconsin before finally landing in Edina, Minnesota in 1973.

Adrian worked as a respected radiologist at Bethesda Hospital and then St. Joseph's Hospital in St. Paul, and was a leading member of St. Paul Radiology. When at home he could be found in his library reading history and listening to jazz or classical music. He loved live music, and he and Jackie treasured their monthly matinees at the Minnesota Orchestra. Ever since the day he turned 40, Adrian was an avid runner, particularly around the lakes of Minneapolis. In his 70s peripheral neuropathy forced him into the gym, or as he put it "the club," in lieu of running, but he remained committed to his daily workouts until the club was closed due to the pandemic.

Adrian retired in 2000 to continue to travel the world with Jackie, and ski, golf and fly fish throughout the western United States. He particularly loved the Rocky Mountains of Montana and Colorado. When the children were still young, he would pack the station wagon and stuff the entire family in to make the drive to the mountains, summer or winter. In his later years, he would sneak out to the family farm in western Wisconsin to sit on the front porch of the cabin he built and gaze over the hills, listen to the breeze flow through the trees surrounding him, and sip a Wild Turkey Old Fashioned (or two).

That's the way his family will lovingly remember him. Adrian was preceded in death by his parents, Alex and Aletha; his brothers, Roland and Charles; his sister, Kathleen; and his beloved wife of 59 years, Jackie, who died just three days before him. He is survived by his four children Christopher, Jonathan, Matthew and Kitty; eight grandchildren and one great grandchild. Also, his dear sisters Ardeth Johnson and Peggy Kapsner, and many nieces and nephews. Funeral arrangements to be announced when it is safe to gather again. In lieu of flowers, donations can be made in the name of Adrian and Jackie Kapsner to the Minnesota Orchestra or St. John's University, Collegeville MN.

We have all had an opportunity to delve inward over the last 12 months and some very creative and profound "musings" have resulted from this introspective time.

Musings

An Introduction to the Poems of Jennifer Ward

Perhaps the most interesting thing about my Covid poems is that I have a muse. From early in the pandemic, Billy Collins, distinguished professor, and former Poet Laureate of the United States, has been reading poems, his own and those of others, on Facebook Live four evenings a week at "about 5:30" for about 20 minutes. His wife, Suzannah, is his tech crew. They banter. He sometimes acknowledges fan comments. He calls it a broadcast.

At first Billy often forgot to clip his mic onto his shirt, fretted about whether he had read a poem already, and subtly counted down the days until the release of his newest book of poems, Whale Day. If you missed a broadcast, you could view it later from his Facebook page. Later, Billy and Suzannah began using an intro of jazz music, and his home office morphed into a little studio with lights and reflective umbrellas. They have learned a lot about copyrighted music and the changeable nature of Facebook. A few of their posts have been taken down. There have been technical difficulties. They have rolled with it all.

It's an ongoing intimate meeting in the tradition of the fireside poets of the Romantic Period. We visit his study. Billy shares that he has a cold, that grandchildren are born, that his house renovations are too loud for sharing today, whatever is the news. He talks about musicians, tells us that "the virus is slowing us down to the speed of poetry." We learn that the Collins's release monarch butterflies, that Billy has been tagged Professor Bebop. Eventually he delivers a private reading complete with firsthand stories of fellow authors and academic insights. Viewership sometimes approaches five thousand people from all around the world. I imagine he has been muse to many, many lapsed writers such as myself. Bravo, Billy.

Existential Dread

by Jennifer Ward

The squirrel catches my eye, a reflection
from street, through upstairs window and
bathroom mirror to me.

His carefree tail twitches gray, rimmed with
dirty tan. His downward head is entirely lost
in fur plumage and concrete.

I watched him yesterday from the
kitchen window: a Cormac McCarthy character
digging for last year's acorns.

Foolish brave, he buried his whole head
into grass and dirt, heedless
of the oak tree's hawk.

Now he tempts death in a frenzied scooping
of seeds and nuts from deep cracks
in the Covid quiet street.

Don't suppose you know us, Squirrel.
We only pretend to care.
We are maskless and texting.

I pull back my hair, dreading the rushing hum
of a car that likely ignores the stop sign,
and fur matching pavement patch...

Nothing good comes of carelessness.

In lock down, I live inside
with my cupboards full of gin and toilet paper,
heeding an ancient internal warning
the squirrel has cast aside.

Hanging Together
by Jennifer Ward

Tonight I made a salad
of the parsley that survived the mild winter
and half a cucumber left over
from last weekend's martinis.

Tomatoes and green onions
washed with a drop of dish soap wilt in the fridge,
and so too the lemons, stripped
of their waxiness, feel sponge soft.

Bulgar, washed and soaked,
is the heroic savior of the whole.
It alone stands firm, plumped,
ready to support the rest.

Bubble Days is inspired by the 2020 pandemic. I painted it in the Spring 2020 while working on our US tax return Form 1040, playing Words With Friends virtually, playing Sudoku, and painting. Hidden in the artwork is the shape of a woman floating on her back, as that was the predominant surrealistic feeling of floating I wanted to capture, both inside the bubble as well as outside the bubble.

- *Eugenia Garcia*

Bubble Days *by Eugenia Garcia*

Cancer
In a Time of Covid

by Art Goodtimes

Strange to be among the target infirmed
at highest risk, after years of
exceptional health & feeling exempt

But we may all end up there too
at the mercy of a virus

that's famous for mutating on the fly
as in bats & pandemics & virulent alleles

That is, if viruses are alive, which we aren't
even sure is true. Maybe they're the real aliens
Saprophytes cocooned among us

or as one Deep Creek artist told us
years ago at Dan & Laurie's art camp
humans are merely vesicles for viruses

Pandemic Perspective
by Erin Robertson

on this first full green-blue day of panicked spring
I cup a little brown mouse in my palm
put my lips to her round warm ear
and whisper
until every last fear has exited my chest
in a slow stream of warm urgent breath
carrying bits of my heart and mind
into her delicate nervous system

she blinks
twitches her whiskers
pats my thumb with her paw
as if to say
oh sweet one
imagine having a nestful of blind babies
surrounded by silent owls -
you never know
when disappointment may come
all you can do
is greet the sun
with whatever semblance of thanks you can muster
any day it deigns to shine

My Corona
by Gail Steckler & C. J. Crane

(sung to the tune of My Sharona)

Ooh my little viral sphere, viral fear
Really goin' out of my mind, Corona
Ooh you make my fever high, my mother cry
Must've caught it from a friend of, my Corona

Never gonna stop, infect lots, an invasive kind
Then it gets on the tongue, into the lungs,
and they fill with dung
My, my, my aye, aye whooo!
M-m-m my Corona

Come a little closer huh, a will ya huh?
Close enough for me to inspire, Corona
Novel virus mystery, come kiss on me
Setting antibodies on fire, Corona

Never going out, stay at home, such an idle mind
Always cleaning up, with the bleach, super strong kind
My, my, my, aye, aye whooo!
M-m-m my Corona
M-m-m my Corona

When you gonna give to me, a test to me
Is it just a matter to sign, Corona
Is it a-a-allergies, a-allergies
Or is it just a game in my mind, Corona

Never going out, stay at home, such an idle mind
Always cleaning up, with the bleach, super strong kind
My, my, my, aye, aye whooo!
M-m-m my Corona
M-m-m my Corona

Presidential Haiku
by Abraham Lincoln and by Joseph Biden

A hidden haiku in Abraham Lincoln's 1861 inaugural address:

"Though passion may have
strained it must not break our
bonds of affection."

And one from Biden's 2021 inaugural address:

"We can join forces
stop the shouting and lower
the temperature."

Made in the USA
Las Vegas, NV
05 May 2021

22477571R00138